All My Darlings

All My Darlings

THOMAS BYRNES

Illustrated by

PAUL GALDONE

New York

THOMAS Y. CROWELL COMPANY

To Ginny

Contents

Contents

I · The Day the House Was Sold

"The trouble is," said Mr. Van Ettig, "it isn't every day you find a family that *needs* a house this big."

Mr. Van Ettig is a real-estate dealer in our town, and a man of wonderful patience. I mention his patience because every spring for the past five or six years he has come to our house at our invitation, sat in the same chair, and listened attentively to our firm avowal that finally, irrevocably, we have decided to move, and will he please handle the sale.

It isn't that we don't like our house any more. We love it. We've loved the place from the moment we first saw it. I admit that at the time we bought it I had certain misgivings about the amount of upkeep it would demand, the fuel it would require, and the rather high taxes. To these objections

1

Ginny, my wife, had answered that it was an ideal home for the children, the grounds were big enough so the older ones could have a pony, and the attic would make a wonderful playroom.

Well, the attic *has* made a wonderful playroom—and so has every other room in the house. The children don't have a pony, but they have two horses, two dogs, six cats, six ducklings, three rabbits, and a parakeet.

Looking at it another way, however, as I do every day from about 6 A.M. to 11 P.M., the upkeep has been considerable, the fuel required would supply the Atlantic fleet for winter maneuvers, and the taxes are as high as the old windmill that stands in a back corner of the property. So for the past few years, after the long, rigorous winter, we have decided to be sensible and look for something easier to manage.

Our neighbors now consider this annual decision as one of the sure-fire signs of spring and a reminder that it's time to start taking down their storm windows.

Why don't we ever go through with our plan? That's hard to say. Certainly it's not the fault of Mr. Van Ettig's salesmanship, as I will try to show.

"Where," Mr. Van Ettig was saying, "can you find a family with nine children these days?" Last year he said, "Where can you find a family with eight children these days?" And the year before that he wanted to know where you could find a family with seven.

These, however, are purely rhetorical questions. All Mr. Van Ettig is trying to do is keep our hopes for a quick sale from soaring too high. Only a very large family would want a house as big as ours. Mr. Van Ettig wants us to face that fact and keep on facing it right up until somebody makes a down payment.

Mr. Van Ettig smiled apologetically. "It isn't that I disapprove of large families," he said, as he has said before. "I think I've told you I come from a family of eleven."

"How wonderful," my wife said.

"My father and mother will celebrate their golden anniversary next month. They still live in the big old house in Joplin."

There was a far-away look in Mr. Van Ettig's eyes.

"Well," he said, rubbing his mustache briskly, "I'd like to go through your house again just to get an idea of its condition. Mind?"

This annual tour through our house is taken, not so much to re-acquaint Mr. Van Ettig with its layout, as to give him an opportunity to point out the various reasons why it could go for much less than the romantic figure we usually have in mind.

"If I were you," Mr. Van Ettig said, as the inspection got under way, "I'd do something about the nicks in that woodwork. Little details like that make a big difference with some people."

He was referring to an express-train stop on the Rainy-Day Railroad, the rolling stock of which consisted of an ancient baby buggy, a wobbly bassinet, and a coaster wagon. Deep scars on the doorframe between living room and dining room attested to the ambition of the young engineers to bring their trains as close to the "station platform" as possible.

In one of the bedrooms the agent's gimlet eyes spotted a cluster of crayon scrawls with which one of the younger children had tried to improve the rose pattern of the wallpaper.

"Could stand a lot of redecorating," Mr. Van Ettig said, "and the floors—I dunno."

Like a pair of criminals being brought back to the scene of their crime, my wife and I tagged along after him as he ruthlessly uncovered every scar and blemish of the year's strenuous living.

With maddening deliberateness he traced a sensitive forefinger over the deep scratches the three year old had made with a skate key on the living-room picture-window sill.

With the tip of a well-shined shoe he gently nudged a brick that had come loose on the fireplace hearth. "They keep secret messages in the cracks," I explained feebly.

A closet door stuck so badly he gave up trying to open it.

"The oldest boy fixed it that way so the younger ones wouldn't get in to upset his football gear," I apologized. We left the closet undisturbed.

In the hallway he *used* to ask, "Stair carpeting stay?" This time he merely looked and moved on. It was obvious the stair carpeting couldn't stay. Parts of it had left already. "They're pretty active kids," I tried to cover up. "We believe in letting the children *live* in a house." Mr. Van Ettig merely nodded.

The inspection over at last, he made a few notes, which he was careful not to let us see, remarked again that it would be hard to find a family big enough to need this type house, and climbed into his car.

He did not start up immediately, but sat staring thoughtfully out across the lawn, where the outlines of a last summer's baseball diamond showed faintly in the grass. My wife and I waited.

"Well," he said, punching the starter button, "it was a tough summer on lawns, wasn't it?"

Ginny and I walked back to the house, thanking the gods of real estate that we finally had enough sense to sell before it collapsed on our heads and the weeds took over completely.

A week later Mr. Van Ettig phoned to tell us he had a prospect who just *might* be interested.

The prospect, it developed, was an expressionless 250-pound male named Turpley, who, as Mr. Van Ettig put it, was beating the bushes for a likely buy before bringing out his wife—an operation, we gathered, that Turpley didn't undertake just any old time.

We greeted them in the driveway and started for the front door. Mr. Van Ettig, however, had planned a more elaborate strategy. Pleasantly but firmly he steered Turpley to a spot fifty or sixty feet out on the grass, made reverent remarks about the cloud formations as if they were part of the deal, then slowly turned Turpley about and whispered, "There!"

And there it was—the long Colonial house, with its dark-green shutters, its rose arbor heavy with vines along the east wall, a profusion of evergreens hugging its foundation, the giant linden tree near the doorway throwing a dappled pattern of sunlight and shadow on the slanting roof. From an upstairs window our five-year-old Tony waved at us gaily to let us know how happy he was that "company" had come.

"It's a wonderful house for children," said my wife in a tiny voice.

I looked at Turpley to see his reaction and concluded that nothing short of a blow in his midriff would change his placid expression.

"How many children do you have?" my wife asked him.

"Mr. Turpley doesn't have any children," the agent answered. "Isn't that what you told me, Mr. Turpley?"

Mr. Van Ettig picked up Turpley's nod and passed it on to the rest of us as if it were the most natural thing in the world for a fellow without children to want a seven-bedroom house.

As we walked through the rooms, we were joined here and there by one or more of the children. In the living room the two oldest boys, fifteen and fourteen, shut off their favorite TV program to follow us.

"You've seen the house before," I growled at them, trying to keep the group to manageable size. I was also trying to stare down their look of hostility at this bare-faced invasion of their home.

"We'll be okay," Kip, the oldest, muttered from his lanky, six-feet-two height. His gunboat-size feet were already shuffling across the carpet in pursuit of the procession. David, shorter, stockier, more nimble than his brother, side-stepped the argument neatly and walked beside Mr. Van Ettig so he wouldn't miss a word.

Meanwhile the agent's salesmanship rippled along at a confident, unhurried pace. "Look at that," he said, giving a wall a resounding whack, "solid as the rock of Gibralter! This place is really built."

We disturbed the twelve- and nine-year-old girls, who were busy playing house in their bedroom. They thought at first we had "company" and smiled their welcome, but the unresponsive faces of the two strangers told them their mistake, and the smiles slowly and reluctantly died. They looked at me for an explanation, but how can you tell two little girls playing house that the house is up for sale? They strung along behind us, silent and baffled.

"Look at those doorframes," Mr. Van Ettig was saying. "Where will you find workmanship like that *these* days?"

He pointed to the ceilings. "Not a crack. That's real plaster."

He touched a door handle lovingly. "Real hardware."

"Wait'll you see the tile in this bathroom," he said, pushing open the partly closed door.

"Hi," he was greeted by four-year-old Tommy, perched comfortably on the seat.

"Oh, my goodness," said Mr. Van Ettig, backing out, "I didn't know—"

"We had to remove the bathroom locks," Ginny explained. "The little ones were always locking themselves in."

Mr. Van Ettig was obviously turning over in his mind the embarrassing possibilities of this arrangement, when Nina, the twelve year old, slipped past him.

"Tommy," she scolded her young brother, "how many times has Daddy told you to whistle when you're in the bathroom?" Nina is the family's stand-in mother.

"I forgot," said Tommy. Then he added, "I wanted to see who it was."

Mary-Jo, a husky three year old, toddled out of the broom closet where, as Ginny discovered later, she had been busy squirting tooth paste into the exhaust vent of the vacuum cleaner. Nina hurriedly closed the closet door.

"That's our hospital in there," she said defiantly. It was obvious the "hospital" was not for sale.

Nor were numerous areas in the older boys' room, which was littered from top to bottom with the treasures of many a summer exploration—a cow's jaw bone, a bird's nest, parts of an old harness, colored stones, and items that defied description. Dave took up his stand in a corner of the room like a Buckingham-Palace guard, his expression cold to Mr. Van Ettig's remark that "real boys live in this house, eh?"

Sympathetically, my wife patted Dave's shoulder and nudged the procession forward to less personalized rooms.

These, however, were hard to find. Even in the master bedroom it was impossible to move without tripping over other claim stakes the children had set out. At one point Mr. Van Ettig had entered a cavernous clothes closet in search of the electric light; when he emerged, trailing Ginny's dressing gown, he discovered that everyone had moved to the window to hear Danielle, the nine year old, explain that the umbrella-shaped hawthorne tree outside was named the fairy tree because real fairies lived in it. "If you stand in this window at night, they signal to you with little lights. We call this window the fairy window."

I thought there was too much of an edge to Mr. Van Ettig's laugh. Danielle notice it, too, and flushed.

"You're right, dear," my wife sprang to her defense, "we *do* see their lights, don't we?"

"This is the small bedroom," Mr. Van Ettig said later, opening the door to the nursery. In the crib, one-year-old Gael Marie was sleeping peacefully. The windows were open, and the curtains stirred gently in the spring air. The odor of the first lilacs filled the room.

For a moment nobody moved. Then the baby stretched, her features flushing and twisting in the luxury of a long, lazy yawn. She opened her blue eyes and, peering through the bars of the crib, smiled at Mr. Turpley.

That stoic's expression remained unchanged, but he cleared his throat. "This house," he said slowly, to the surprise of everyone, "is a wonderful house for children."

My wife immediately left the room. When she caught up with us a few minutes later, her eyes were red rimmed.

A year ago at this point Mr. Van Ettig would have frowned

and suggested we leave him alone with the prospective buyer. Now he merely sighed. He knew the signs.

We continued the tour of the house, but the agent's heart wasn't in it. He slapped a few beams in the basement to show how solid they were, but the old steam was gone.

Out in the driveway again beside the car, he let Mr. Turpley take one more look around, and we all looked with him. The sun was setting on the west line of the property, silhouetting the playhouse I had made for the children the year before. Down in the little meadow between our house and the main road two neighbor children were trudging up through the tall grass, and our collie and spaniel were bounding down to meet them. A wren chittered from the wren house Kip had built in the fairy tree. . . .

I like Mr. Van Ettig. When I met him in town a few days later, he showed no rancor. In fact I thought I detected a certain wistfulness in the gray eyes peering at me from above the wispy mustache. What was he thinking of, I wonder? The big family of eleven and the old house in Joplin?

"You were wise to take your house off the market," he said, as he has said before. "Where would you find a place so well suited for the kids?"

"You're right," I agreed. "And where would you find workmanship like that these days?"

I invited him to drop over and pay us a social call some time, and he said he would—soon.

But I knew from experience he wouldn't be around again for at least another year.

2 · "Have You Been Talking Marriage?"

The marriage that so far has produced nine children started in a way that close observers, for a long time, called "All wrong from the very beginning."

The "very beginning" took place the day after I began work in the fiction department of a Chicago newspaper. My department editor and myself were having our morning coffee in the building's drug store when a tall girl, slender as a reed, entered and sat down beside us.

The editor, who knew everybody on the paper, and thought everybody should know everybody else, promptly introduced us.

"This is young Tommy Byrnes," he said, "a fine, upstanding Irish boy, who intends to get married the minute he finds the right girl." To me he said, "Ginny here is regarded as one of the most beautiful girls in the Middle West."

I was entirely willing to agree. Long, light-brown hair framed a face of well-defined planes, from which a full, yet sensitive, mouth sent its smile straight to the pit of my stomach. I remember the smile because there were moments during the conversation when I felt she was not smiling but laughing, and not at anything that was said, but at me; that is, when she wasn't ignoring me completely.

The editor did most of the talking—for which I was thankful. This gave me more time to observe. I can be very objective about that first meeting now, looking back at it across sixteen years, but at the moment I was self-conscious and gauche.

When we parted, I was sure I had made something less than an "impression."

Later, my fears were confirmed.

"The first reports are in," said the editor next morning. "I hate to say it, but I'm afraid you're not in the running. She thinks you're one of the funniest-looking people she has ever seen."

"Nice of her to say so," I muttered.

"She particularly noticed your blue-checkered shirt, polka-dot tie and white-duck pants. You were chewing gum, sipping a coke, and smoking a pipe all at the same time. Then with your pipe going like a furnace, you tried to light a cigarette."

"Very observing, isn't she?" I said, thinking how difficult life would be with a girl like that. "I can tell you one thing— it'll be a long time before she sees *me* at such close range again."

Ginny's next view of me at close range was across her desk, next day, when I asked her out to lunch. She pleaded a previous engagement, but even while she was turning me down I thought there was less amusement and more friendliness in her smile than the first time I saw it. Besides, I had been careful to wear a plain shirt and tie, and my pipe was out of sight in my pocket.

Next day I repeated the invitation, and she set a date for several days later. I had an uncomfortable feeling that there was no time to lose.

The results of our luncheon meeting can best be described in the words of another friend, whose desk was opposite Ginny's. "She came back to the office, slapped her purse and hat down, and said she had never met such a boring person in all her life. 'All he did was talk about himself.' "

"Anything else?" I asked.

"Oh, yes—she doesn't like the name Tom."

After my wounded feelings had completely healed over (which they did in about fifteen minutes), I arranged another meeting on the plea that I had to clear up the misunderstanding about my luncheon talkativeness. On our first evening date, a few days later, I convincingly proved my point, through a discourse several hours long, that I was really the strong silent type, and my gabbiness had been nothing more than an over-done effort to create a good impression.

In the face of such logic she could only agree. Two months after we first met, we were married.

But it was not as simply done as it may sound. Here again the signs and portents were all wrong. At least I was certain my parents would consider them all wrong.

As the only son of a father and mother who held with the grip of a bulldog to the conviction that a good salary, a large

bank account and a long courtship are indispensable conditions for a happy marriage, I foresaw all kinds of difficulty in
even talking around the fringes of the subject at home.

In the past I had never been able to discover what they
considered a good salary, but I was sure my thirty-eight dollars a week was far from being *it*. And since their own year-
long courtship had often been referred to by my mother as a
whirlwind affair, I was certain the two months Ginny and I
had known each other would be viewed as scarcely beyond
the "pleased-to-meet-you" stage.

But in addition to their attitude toward marriage, I had to
consider their attitude, especially my mother's, toward me.

This could best be compared, even in my twenty-sixth year,
to the attitude of a mother grizzly protecting her cub from a
pack of hounds. The hounds in my case were anything from
wet feet to the neighborhood bully. Was it cold enough outside to wear a sweater? I would have to wear two. I still
cringe when I think of being paged one night during a high-
school dance at a downtown hotel and being told by a smirk-
ing bellhop in the presence of a dozen of my pals that my
mother had dropped off my overshoes and I was to wear them
home because it had started to snow.

This passion for protecting me was strongest where young
ladies were concerned. Did I ask the same girl for two dates
in a row? This was evidence that things were getting pretty
serious and must be looked into. I would be cautioned darkly
against tying up my affections in any way that might jeopard-
ize my future, whatever it was at the time. Any girl who
went out with Byrnes more than once could be sure that her
morals, intentions and upbringing had passed my mother's
careful scrutiny.

It must be said in mother's defense, however, that perhaps

without the overshoes that stormy night, I *would* have caught the cold I didn't catch; and without her brooding solicitude in social matters I might have found myself ineligible for marriage to Ginny. "Early and provident fear is the mother of safety," says the orator Burke, who may have known what he was talking about at that.

To tell such parents that I intended to marry a girl I had known for only two months, on no bank account, and a salary that might have come out of a piggy bank would have been like telling them I intended to practice Free Love. They had met Ginny many times after I first introduced her, and seemingly they liked her—but only as a friend who would someday marry someone else.

Sooner or later, however, the news of our intentions would have to be broken, so one evening, while my father was loosening his belt after dinner and Mother was reading the evening paper, I worked up enough courage to approach the subject—at what I thought was a diplomatic tangent.

"Dad," I said carelessly, "how much money do you think a fellow ought to be making before he gets married?"

To Dad this was as impersonal and theoretical a question as "Do you think what's-his-name will better the national-high-jump record this year?" He finished a yawn, removed his glasses and studied the ceiling. "Well—" he began.

"Junior!" My mother's voice cut to the heart of the problem with the speed of a rapier thrust. "Have you been talking marriage to that young lady?"

"God Almighty!" My father straightened in his chair. "Is it *yourself* you're talking about?"

"Why not?" I quavered.

He stared at me mutely for a moment as if unwilling to believe that such a preposterous thing could be mentioned under his roof.

"Are you crazy?" he finally exploded. "Why you're not making enough money to support a canary!" The canary has always been my father's favorite reference point in any comparison of the different stages of financial ineptitude.

"Well?" Tight-lipped, my mother insisted on a direct answer. Had I mentioned marriage to that young lady?

I admitted I had.

It is impossible to transcribe the resulting remarks in their proper order. There was no order. There were star-like explosions of questions, denunciations, warnings, lamentations and prophecies, almost Biblical in their heroic proportions. Two themes became dominant. One, the economic, expounded by my father with frequent references to the canary, held that a man had no right to take on the responsibilities of marriage without a nest egg to fall back on, and a darn good income to make sure the nest egg would never have to be touched.

The other theme, more sociological, was developed by my mother with dismal apothegms about the folly of sacrificing my brilliant future and a promising career just to follow a silly infatuation.

Nothing was settled. Talked out, completely overwhelmed, I let the storm die, which it did slowly, with occasional sniffles from Mother and rustling of her newspaper, and my father's oft-repeated statement that, by George, *he* was going to bed.

The scene at Ginny's house, where she, too, had broached the subject, was much the same, I learned next day, though not so violent. Her parents could see no security for their daughter in marrying a fellow whose only plans for the future seemed to be that he "wanted to write something some time."

Subsequent attempts to win parental cooperation only re-
sulted in more violent reactions, so without further storm we
made our final arrangements without telling anyone.

"A man will leave his father and mother and will cling to
his wife," says St. Paul, stating nothing but the unvarnished
truth.

If he had added, "Even without his father and mother
knowing anything about it," and described the attendant
complications, then the Marriage Day Mass, in which his
words are read, would be considerably longer than it is.

To begin with, there was the bother of the blood test—and
the extra bother of locating a doctor who didn't know my
parents and wouldn't tell them my plans. (The regular family physician would have had them on the phone before my
blood had cooled in the container.)

What made this search doubly troublesome was the fact
that I am one of those clumsy individuals who is always
bumping into someone's third cousin who had lunch with Aunt
Maggie the other day, and what's this I hear about your getting married?

Once, a few years later, when I had worked long enough to
scrape together the makings of a small bank account, I enter-
tained the delusion that its size was nobody's business but
mine, and so passed up the neighborhood bank, where friends
and neighbors were employed, in favor of a larger and, I be-
lieved, more impersonal bank in the Chicago Loop. Cross-
examined by one of the VP's until I thought they were going
to groom me for counter-espionage work in another bank, I
finally got up to leave, serenely confident that my financial
status would remain as secret as the strategy of the next
World Series. The VP, however, motioned me to stay seated.

"I notice," he said, "you work for such-and-such." He smiled a tiny smile.

"Yep," I said, fighting down an impulse to deny everything I had just told him.

"Know Joe So-and-so?" he asked.

I did, and I disliked him as intently as it is possible to dislike *any* so-and-so, but all I did now was nod my head dumbly. I knew what was coming. "You know him too, eh?" I asked, with forced amiability.

"I ought to," smiled the VP, "he's my son."

These invisible ties with the outer world don't usually lead to the embarrassing revelations I am always expecting, but their effect on the nervous system is that of a time bomb that may never go off but nevertheless sizzles.

It was about the same with the doctor. I had climbed aboard a street car, early one evening, with a collection of short stories under my arm. When I finish the first story, I told myself, I will get off and go to the first doctor I find.

The first doctor I found was a talkative, lion-maned old codger, who kept saying, "I'm sure I've seen you someplace before." Did I know Bill What's-his-name back at school? Knew him like a brother. Well, well. Bill knew *his* boy, and maybe I was one of the old bunch Joe (that's *his* boy) used to have up at the house on Friday nights for billiards in the basement. I guessed that was about the way it was. Well, well. So I was eloping, eh? A very serious business. The doctor hated to think how *he'd* feel if Joe ever ran away and got married without telling anybody. And come to think of it, wasn't my father the Thomas S. Byrnes who used to work with Whatcha-ma-callum on the Northwest Side? The same. A fine man, salt of the earth. Too bad you've decided to elope.

Shaken and short of blood by several ounces (he had spilled the first sample in his concern over Thomas S. Byrnes' feelings), I staggered out into the blizzardy night, knowing that a hundred eyes were following me. For days I watched my parents warily, wondering when they'd be tipped off.

And it was the same with the priest to whom we went to make arrangements for "a quiet ceremony." So I was the nephew of Monsignor Byrnes and Father Ed Byrnes. Fine priests. Knew them well. What did *they* think of all this elopement business? What? They don't know? Not going to tell them? Why not?

The marriage-bureau clerk didn't know me—or at least he didn't admit it—but he did his utmost to get us to appear on a "Meet-the-Bride-and-Groom-To-Be" radio interview, which was already on the air in the next room. The fact that we were being married in secret only sharpened his efforts. "Think what a *show* that will make," he kept saying. I was convinced for days that hidden microphones *had* interviewed us and that my mother had heard every word.

During all these preparations, and many more, I suffered from the same misgivings Benedict Arnold must have known when plotting the surrender of West Point—and with the same feverish conviction that the plot, if discovered, would bring consequences just as shattering.

The climax came on the morning of the wedding when I tried to slip out of the house past my mother and father, with my briefcase bulging like a fatted calf with clean shirt, underwear, sox and pajamas.

"Breakfast is ready," my father said, as I entered the kitchen with hat and coat.

"Not this morning," I said. "I'm not hungry." It was the first morning in twenty-six years that I hadn't been hungry. So

I might as well have said that all my teeth had just dropped out.

"You look sort of pale," said my mother. "Do you have a headache?"

"A dilly," I said.

"We have lamb chops," said my father temptingly. Nobody could broil lamb chops like my father. "With butter," he added. Nobody could smother lamb chops in butter like my father.

"Do you *have* to go to work today?" asked my mother.

"Today of all days," I said.

"What in the world do you have stuffed in that briefcase?" asked my mother. Nobody could ask questions like my mother.

"I—I'm playing handball tonight," I stammered. I pointed to the briefcase. "Sweat shirts, sox, and—things."

"Glory be to God," said my father. "You can't play handball on an empty stomach. I *know*." Nobody could play handball like my father. *I* know.

I finally convinced them I'd be all right, told them not to worry, gave them what I felt was the Judas kiss, and went down the back steps. As I turned out the backyard gate for the shortcut to the railroad station, I looked back. My father's white hair was visible in the window of the pantry, where, I knew, he was leaning over the refrigerator to wave a cheery good-by, as he did every morning. I waved too.

"A man will leave his father and mother . . ."

In the sacristy of the church, I waited for Ginny, and composed my letter of explanation and, I feared, farewell, to my parents. After the ceremony I would give it to a Western Union messenger, who would take it directly to their house.

"Dear Mother and Dad," I wrote, "I'm sorry it has to be

done this way, but I think that with all of us feeling as we do, it's the best way. The way *I* feel makes it all seem right. This morning Ginny and I are being married in Holy Name Cathedral. I know that if I had told you at the last minute, you would have come. But I'm afraid the coming would have been too much of an ordeal, and the telling would have been impossible."

I looked about the room for a concluding thought. The air was sweetly scented with a sacristy's never-lost fragrance of incense, a fragrance I knew so well as a boy serving Benediction. From the opposite wall the figure on the cross looked down.

"There's nothing to worry about," I ended lamely. "I have money enough to take care of us." I told them I would always love them, and signed good-by.

There were footsteps on the stairs outside. The door of the sacristy opened.

"Virginia is here," the priest said, and stood back to let her pass.

My heart lifted like a bird. "My darling, my darling!"

". . . and he will cling to his wife."

As we stood at the foot of the altar I reflected that my salary for that week had been paid in advance for a furnished, one-room apartment not far away and my total cash assets were a ten-dollar check I had received in the nick of time for a short magazine article I had written a month before. It was all we had with which to face the immediate problems of food and clothing. I recollect, however, that neither of us cared.

A few days later my talent for running into people who knew other people I knew caught up with me again. At the moment that I was emerging from a delicatessen with the makings of our dinner, a former classmate, whom I hadn't seen in five years, entered.

"Old Tom!" he hailed me.

"Old Joe," I saluted.

No sense in keeping the glad tidings from Old Joe. What current friends of mine did Joe know? Not a one, I was sure. I told him the whole story, complete with address and phone number of the apartment hotel.

Ginny and I hadn't finished dinner before there was a message that a friend of mine was on the hall phone. Old Joe, I thought, trying to arrange a little get-together.

A little get-together was being arranged all right, but not the kind I envisioned.

"Well, Thomas," said a familiar, and thank God, friendly voice. "So you did it at last. Congratulations."

"Well, I'll be hanged! How in the world did *you* find out so soon?"

"I've been trying all over to locate you; your parents are frantic. They asked me to help find you. Five minutes ago who do I run into but old Joe What's-his-name and he told me the good news."

The voice belonged to one of my former college professors much admired by my father because both men had been born in Ireland.

"How did Mother and Dad take it?" I asked.

"Better call them up," he said.

Mother's tearful voice asked us to come right over.

Her eyes were red, her face long and sorrowful as if the services at the grave had just been completed. Wordlessly, she motioned Ginny and me inside.

"Where's Dad?" I asked, preparing for another bout with the canary.

"He's not home yet. Ah, Junior," she said, "he's a changed man."

I was to find out after a while that my letter had indeed been a severe shock, especially to my father, who saw it not so much as a revolutionary move on my part as a betrayal of manly companionship, a refusal to take him into my confidence. He had sought consolation from his brother, Father Ed, who brought him up sharply by stating that in *his* considered opinion I had done the most sensible thing in my life. "It will do Tom a world of good," said the man of God.

I was denied this consoling bit of information for the time being, however, and sat there in stupid silence watching my mother twist her handkerchief. Finally she said, "What did you mean when you said you had plenty of money?"

I took a deep breath. I knew the worst was behind me. "Oh," I said, a little giddy from the strain, "nothing to worry about in *that* department. I have my salary and—and there's the magazine check—and don't worry about *me*."

Through the doorway to the dining room I could see the table set for dinner. There were places for all of us.

When my father arrived, he embraced me. Then he turned and embraced my wife. No one spoke. He stood back, holding Ginny's arms. His eyes were red, but he was not crying. He said simply, "You're very welcome."

Dinnertime was filled with arrangements, made as unemotionally as you would make them at a death bed, for moving my clothes, books, and typewriter to my new home.

Afterwards, my father said to me, "You and I will go out to the store now and get you some groceries." He seemed obsessed with the idea that Ginny and I were about to starve to death. The food he bought on that one shopping trip kept us supplied for more than a week. Even years after we were married, Dad scarcely let a Saturday afternoon go by without bringing us food for the week-end, especially large, juicy beef roasts. Marriage or no marriage, he was still the family patriarch. We were all his responsibility.

The next day we took him up to see our tiny apartment. "Glory be to God," he said, "are they charging rent for *this?*"

"You should see the rent they're asking for *some* of the places we've looked at," I said defensively.

"Ridiculous. You must move in with us, at least for the time being. It will give you a chance to save some money."

We put off moving for a few happy months, but he became so insistent (and we *weren't* saving any money), that at last we gave in. But just for a little while, we told ourselves.

In spite of my parents' efforts to make us welcome, it was not a happy arrangement. We missed the heady feeling of independence we had learned to prize, and the loss was not made up for by mother's protracted lessons in biscuit making and salad seasoning, or by father's frequent admonitions on the importance of saving money (we *still* weren't saving it).

We stayed for a month or two, then moved out to another and larger apartment than our first. It had become apparent one exciting morning that, unless the usual indications were all wrong, we would need a room for a nursery before another nine months were up. "When we bring our baby home," Ginny said, "he must come to a place of his own."

"You're right," said the patriarch. "You must have your own place now. The children make all the difference."

3 · Always Room for One More

"But what are you going to *name* the baby?"

When asked by the relatives (from their perch on the nearest family tree), this little poser is more a challenge than a question. People who were most critical of our marriage in the beginning are usually the most vehement in demanding that honor be done some family favorite by naming the newcomer after him.

When Kip, the oldest, was born, Ginny and I were determined to avoid this common problem by ignoring it. We would name the baby after nobody in *either* family. We would name him Christopher, after the third-century saint, who seemed safely beyond the lineal claims of anybody this side of Heaven.

Avoiding this problem by ignoring it, however, was like avoiding a traffic accident by ignoring the stop signs.

My father, a firm believer in the old custom of naming the first male after its male parent, assumed without question that his name would be Thomas.

When the baby was born, I called home.

"Hello?" shouted my father, who was waiting for the call.

"Hello, Dad," I said, exuberantly, "Christopher has just arrived."

"Who?" said my father.

"Christopher."

"Christopher *who?*" asked my father, suspiciously.

"Christopher Byrnes."

There was a long silence. A soft, sustained, tuneless whistling sound told me my father was setting his lips grimly before delivering a particularly devastating remark.

I tried to change the subject. "He's a fine baby," I said.

"God Almighty," breathed my father. This was merely to gain time. More was coming. "There isn't a banana peddler between here and the Chicago River that isn't named Christopher. What in God's name are you trying to do?"

"But we *like* it."

"*You* like it," he said, sarcastically. "What's the matter— aren't the old Irish names good enough for you? What's wrong with Patrick or Dennis or John or Phillip or your *own* name?"

I didn't think it was quite the time to tell him that my own name and most of the others were hardly the exclusive property of the Irish. I concentrated on the baby's fine appearance, his good health and general measurements.

"Well," said my father at last, "I'll come down and see him." But it was obvious he didn't expect to see much.

He stood at the nursery window watching the baby for a

long time, his face set, at first, in grim determination not to be taken in by anything named Christopher. But by degrees the stern lines softened, and when a nurse (bless her) suggested that the baby was the picture of its father, who (she went on) was the picture of *his* father, the miracle of the succession of fingers and toes and noses and foreheads and eyes and mouths and cheekbones was too much for him. He began to cry—the soft, soundless crying of a man who never cries. He held my arm tightly in mute symbol of the unbroken thread that had spun its way from the hills of Wicklow and Tipperary, through an immigrant's early loneliness, to this baby, in this hospital, in America. The baby was himself, his son, his grandson, and the father of his father's fathers. Dad would live to see the births of our second boy and our first girl, but there would never be another moment quite like this.

Later, Ginny said to him, "Didn't you have a brother named Dennis?"

"Now, now," said my father. "Don't change it just for me."

"But Dennis Christopher," said Ginny. "Don't you like that?"

"Dennis is a fine name."

"And it goes so well with Christopher."

"Dennis Christopher," said my father.

And so it was.

We were getting out of the car in front of the church for the christening of our second.

"Now remember," Ginny said. "It's not too late."

"Too late for what?" I asked.

"To change his name, of course."

"But we've told everybody his name is going to be Stephen."

"Not everybody."

"Everybody *I* talked to."

"But wasn't there a time when we thought Michael—"

"Good Lord!"

"Do you *like* Stephen—I mean *really* like it?"

"Of course I like it."

"I mean *really?*"

By now we were climbing the church steps.

"But, darling," she was saying, "when you stop to think— Steve Byrnes. I don't know."

"Okay," I sighed. "Michael then."

"The other children would call him Mike."

"Why not? That would be his name, wouldn't it?"

We paused for a minute in the vestibule while the god-father and godmother carried whatever-his-name-was-at-the-time to the baptismal font.

"Doesn't Mike sound kind of—rough?"

"What then?"

"Anthony?"

"They'd call him Tony. I thought we didn't like that."

"I think it's cute. Of course the name I *really* like is David. You know that."

"I like David, too. Why did we change?"

"I wish I knew."

"All right then—David."

"Well—if you're *sure.*"

When the priest asked the godfather for the baby's name, he was told, "Stephen."

"No," Ginny stage whispered from a front pew, "it's David now."

"My fault," the godfather said. "I haven't checked since we left home."

At the christening party afterwards, we accepted silver spoons, cups, coverlets and a savings bond, separately inscribed to Stephen and Michael. One cup, for some reason, was engraved "Hugh."

"Hugh," said Ginny reflectively. "Hugh Byrnes. You know . . . I *like* that."

Our first three children caused the spectators no concern at all. True, three were a fraction over the national average, and should have served as a warning of bigger things to come, but then what's a fraction of a baby among friends?

The fourth they explained away laughingly as a "nice, round number." Their attitude stiffened a bit at the fifth and sixth, and I began to hear such hopeful comments as *"That* ought to do you for a while, eh, old boy?"

The faint-of-heart gave up entirely on the seventh. Only the out-and-out liberals hung on, fortifying their loyalty by recalling the good old days when seven children were nothing more than a nice-sized family.

But at eight the jig was up. The whole thing had gotten completely out of hand. Even the roundness of the number was no excuse. In complete abandon, they took to asking (shakily at first), "How soon can we expect Number Nine?"

It wasn't long before I was able to tell them.

To their surprise, Ginny's attitude toward having so many children is anything but one of sufferance. After the birth of Kip (Dennis Christopher), her first words, spoken on the hazy edges of the anesthesia from which she was emerging, were, "I want four boys and two girls."

"How silly of me to have been so conservative," she said

after the birth of our seventh. "Imagine not having this one!"

With Ginny the whole problem is simply a question of whether you like children or don't like them. And if you do, why should you consider them a burden in themselves? She instinctively has no truck with the popular notion that you can have too much of a good thing. If a thing is good, the more of it the merrier.

Each time a baby is on the way, ads for layettes, baby buggies, cribs, playpens, and bassinets are quoted as if written by Shakespeare. Books and magazine articles on infant care and child raising are read with undiminished wonder.

"Look, dear," Ginny will say, lifting her nose from the latest article on bringing up the young, "you *are* supposed to spank them when they're naughty, that is, after they're old enough to know."

"If you're worrying that they've missed out on spankings, relax. I took care of them."

Her face clouds over. "I'm afraid you spank them too hard. You seem so mad."

"When I hit 'em, I *am* mad. As George Bernard Shaw said, never strike your child except in anger."

"That's ridiculous—and dangerous, too."

"But when I'm feeling good, I just can't bring myself to walk up to one of them and suddenly bop him."

Her face brightens. She hasn't even heard me. "This one is going to be the most wonderful of all."

"Absolutely."

Caught up in their mother's excitement over the coming baby, the children lose no time in dreaming up their own versions of the name, sex and character of the unborn. The diversity of ideas often creates the impression among the neighbors that we're expecting quintuplets.

Only when the scary hour of departure for the hospital draws near do their spirits falter. Then the older ones grow more sober, and one by one, in quiet moments, ask me, "Nothing could *happen* to Mummy, could it?" The babies, sensing the others' concern, seem to fall downstairs oftener, stub their toes or do anything that provides an excuse for extra mothering.

But with the first news that the baby has come, and Mummy is fine, their joy bursts and blazons like fireworks.

As it did with the coming of Tony.

It was six o'clock in the morning when I arrived home from the hospital. The house, which in desperation had been left in the care of the older boys, was quiet. I was just deciding that seven o'clock would be soon enough to waken them when I heard Danielle, then four, get out of bed upstairs and patter into the big bedroom.

Immediately there was a loud demand to know where Mummy and Daddy were; and in seconds the rest of the brood were racing down the stairs, two-year-old Peggy puffing along in the rear.

"Daddy! Did Mummy have the new baby yet?" I was surrounded, stormed and overwhelmed.

I told them the news.

"A brother!" they shrieked. The girls danced and hopped about the room. The boys did a jig and repeated over and over, "A boy! That makes it even—three and three!"

"The next one will be a girl," said Nina.

"But where's Mummy?" asked Danielle.

"In the hospital—where do you suppose?" David informed her. By this time he knew that mothers and babies and hospitals all went together somehow—and stayed together for several days.

"Now look," I said, "let's get organized. You kids are going to be late for school."

"Aw, Daddy, do we have to go to school today?" asked Nina, who is always ready to play any celebration for all it's worth.

"You sure do."

"But first we have to call Mummy."

"It's too early," I said. "She's probably asleep."

"There'll be a night nurse to answer the phone, won't there?" asked Kip, the logician.

"Well," I said, giving in, "we'll try anyway."

Against a background of arguments over who would talk to Mummy first, I managed to get the hospital on the phone. A series of fast, erratic clicks, however, told me that the night switchboard operator was having her hands full. An angry feminine voice came on the line and identified itself as belonging to Miss Garvey on Four. "Jonesey says operate," Miss Garvey hissed down the wire at me, "so right away I'm expected to perform miracles."

"I beg your pardon," I interrupted. "I'd like to talk to Mrs. Byrnes in maternity."

"Well, of all the nerve!" was Miss Garvey's reaction, and the phone went dead.

When I reached the hospital again, I was informed by still another voice that no calls were put through during feeding hours.

"But how *is* she?" I persisted.

"As well as can be expected," came the stock answer that has terrorized stouter hearts than mine. The room suddenly seemed very cold.

"What's the matter, Daddy?" the kids asked, reading my face.

"There's nothing wrong, is there?" I shouted into the phone, but the voice was gone.

"Is Mummy all right?" Nina asked, going white.

"She's fine, fine," I said, "but just the same I'm going to call the doctor."

"Mummy must be sick then," David figured.

Peggy began to cry.

"Is she *very* sick?" Danielle asked, her lips quivering.

"Gosh," said Kip, then took a long swallow.

Danielle began to cry.

"I want Mummy," Peggy sobbed.

"Be quiet!" I yelled. "I'm calling the doctor!"

As always in times of stress, Kip and Dave sought each other's company and stood shivering, their eyes as big as light bulbs.

In a fever of fear, I called the doctor's home, but was sleepily informed by his wife that he was busy delivering another baby. How soon they forget, I thought.

"But don't worry," his wife soothed. "I know everything is just fine or he would have called you. He told me you have a *wonderful* baby."

My face must have shown my relief, for immediately the crying stopped, and the word went around that Mummy was fine.

"Of course she's fine!" I laughed, getting up from the phone. "She's always fine, isn't she?"

"Nothing ever happens to Mummy, does it?" Kip grinned.

"Nothing ever happens to Mummy!" they all chorused.

4 · Surprise, Surprise!

No birth in the family is complete without some kind of big surprise for Mummy on her return from the hospital. Many times, however, the plans have been so ambitious that the intended surprise was still in the embryonic stages when she arrived home.

Once, during her absence, we undertook to redecorate the kitchen and breakfast nook. To call in a decorator would have been the sensible thing, but then the surprise would have lacked the personal touch. Also, it would have been too expensive. So after a few hasty councils with the older children, I decided to take on the work myself in the evenings.

The two older boys—eight and nine at the time—were enthusiastic about helping, but their value was limited by the

33

fact that they inevitably fell asleep around nine o'clock. So in addition to mixing paint and hanging wallpaper, I had the job of undressing two unconscious children and carrying them upstairs to bed. I finally convinced them that we'd save time all around if they'd ignore the whole project and go to bed as they usually did, under their own power. They accepted this idea reluctantly and missed no opportunity to point out that if I'd only let them help, the work could have been done twice as fast.

But even with the children out of my way, the time limitations proved too great, and Ginny arrived home to find her usually clean and orderly kitchen in chaos. The smell of paint, which always gave her a headache, filled the house from basement to roof. The work area in the kitchen was ninety percent unusable because of paint cans, mixing sticks, pots of soaking brushes, and sheets of old newspapers intended to keep the counters clean. The color of the freshly painted walls, we discovered too late, matched nothing within a mile of the house.

Ginny got as far as the dining room, spotted the confusion through the joining doorway, and sat down and cried.

Numbly, I patted her shoulder.

"You're so sweet," she sobbed. "You're all so sweet." We were never sure whether she wept for joy or horror.

Another time, the biggest of the bedrooms was selected as the field of operation. I arose on the morning of the day I was to bring Ginny and the new baby home—a Sunday—and realized that at least three more days of work would be needed to make the room habitable.

Fortunately I had set the alarm for 4 A.M., which at least gave me a good start. But by nine o'clock I was still more than two and a half days away from the finished job, with wide patches of old wallpaper stubbornly refusing to let go.

Then a wonderful thing happened. The telephone rang.

"How are you coming with the bedroom?" Jack Leslie, a neighbor, asked.

I tried, out of false pride, to pass the thing off as a lead-pipe cinch, but some of my anxiety must have shown in my voice, for a few minutes later, Jack was knocking at the back door, a bucket and sponges in his hand.

"Charley Ostermann's coming over too," Jack said, "and maybe Jim Bagget, if his wife can get him up in time. Now where's that old wall paper that won't come off?"

In no time at all the stubborn wallpaper was peeling off as easily as the skin of an orange, and a total of five neighbors were industriously sizing walls, washing down woodwork, painting and hanging paper.

At frequent intervals Ginny called from the hospital and impatiently wanted to know why I wasn't coming to get her. Didn't I *want* her to come home? Sniffles and tiny whimperings sputtered across the wire.

"Of course I do, but there are a few things I have to take care of first."

"But what *are* they?"

Be calm, I told myself, she's still weak.

"Just tell her it's a big surprise," the neighbors advised from the bedroom.

"It's a big surprise," I said shakily.

"Not another redecorating job," she begged. "Not that."

"Oh, no—not that."

"I can't stand this place another minute," she sobbed. "You don't love me, or you'd have come for me hours ago."

"I *do* love you," I whispered, trying to keep this avowal as private as possible.

"I hear something," Ginny insisted, "like the slap of paint-brushes."

"I was swatting a fly," I said. "I'll get you in a few more minutes."

Several phone calls later, the job was done. I threw on my overcoat and raced for the hospital.

When we returned an hour later, the neighbors were gone, but they had left the room looking like a magazine ad. They had not only cleaned up after themselves, but their wives had put flowers around the room on nearly every surface big enough to hold a vase, and had set the table in the breakfast nook for a cozy Sunday supper for two. There were cold chicken and ham, relishes, hot biscuits, and a bottle of sauterne. The teapot sat waiting for the water.

"How beautiful!" Ginny said. "How sweet and thoughtful!"

We sat for almost a minute before the food, just the two of us, touching nothing, but thinking of the people whose kindliness had saved the day.

Then we reset the table with more plates and silverware to accommodate the clamoring children.

But the most ambitious surprise of all—and one which seemed the essence of simplicity at the time—was the purchase of the Good Samaritan.

"How will we surprise Mummy this time?" the children were asking, even before Ginny and I had left for the hospital.

"No more redecorating," I insisted.

They agreed that redecorating was out.

"A present of some kind," Kip suggested. "A real *big* present."

"I have it," said David. "How about a dog?"

Well, how about a dog? We were momentarily dogless, so the suggestion seemed the most natural thing in the world.

"Mummy loves dogs," we all agreed. "But what kind would it be?"

We considered the small dogs first, but found ourselves drifting, with considerable prompting from the boys, toward what breeders euphemistically call the working-dog class, the big fellows like the shepherd and the collie.

"Hey," said David again, "how about a great Dane?"

Maybe this was overdoing things a bit, but the more we discussed the idea, the better it sounded. Why *not* a great Dane? A noble breed. Loyal, loving, devoted, and by all accounts, a perfect pet for children.

I thought of the many romantic references I had seen to this giant animal—in story books, where the Dane invariably stood between some helpless toddler and the brink of doom or in advertisements, where with unflinching gaze he stared down everything from foreclosures to pyorrhea.

Who could resist a great Dane? Not us.

A purchase of such importance, however, is not made lightly. You don't simply go to the nearest great-Dane dealer and say, "I want a great Dane," the way you'd say, "I want a pound of hamburger." For one thing you want to be very certain of your source of supply. You inquire, first, among your friends, very casually, as if you've been mulling over the problem for several months and there is no great hurry. Since it isn't every friend who can put his hand on a great Dane at a moment's notice, this feeling-out period can be rather long. In our case the trail didn't begin to get warm until the day we took Ginny to the hospital.

I was backing the car out of the garage to have it in readi-

ness, when the milkman came to make his delivery and
stopped, as he usually does, to talk about the weather.

"Say," I mentioned casually, "I don't suppose you know
where I could pick up a good great Dane?"

The milkman proved to be a gold mine of information. In
fact, he had once raised great Danes himself, but because of
an allergy to dog dander he had to give them up. However,
he had a cousin in Butte, Montana. And the cousin's father-
in-law lived somewhere in San Pedro, California, and *he* was
raising great Danes right now.

The milkman promised he would have his wife write the
cousin, whose father-in-law raised the dogs, and tell him to
get in touch with me.

On the way to the hospital, Ginny wanted to know what
I was looking so happy about, but I said it must be the
excitement of having another baby on the way.

There followed then a long series of telegrams and long-
distance phone calls, from girl's father to girl to husband to
milkman to me. But I knew all this trouble would eventually
pay dividends.

A final telegram from the cousin (collect) said: "Have
Duke, brindle great Dane, disposition aggressive but not
dangerous. For twenty-five dollars more, have Sonia, fawn
color, much more authentic neck."

We decided if we were going to have a great Dane at all,
it might just as well be one with an authentic neck, so I
posted a letter and check to the milkman's cousin, who, I
understood, would forward it to his father-in-law.

Next came a period of anxious waiting, which took us right
up to the day Ginny expected to come home. By three o'clock
in the afternoon there was still no response from California.
Meanwhile we received the usual impatient calls from the

imprisoned Ginny, who demanded to know, once more, why didn't we call for her and didn't we love her any more?

At six o'clock in the evening, unable to stall her any longer, I went to the hospital and brought Ginny and the baby home.

"I might as well tell you," I said, as we turned into the driveway, "there's no big surprise this time. Things just didn't work out the way we'd planned."

"Oh, darling, what difference does it make?" she said warmly, giving my arm a squeeze. "Just coming home is enough. I don't even *want* any surprise."

The Western-Union messenger was waiting at the front door.

"Sonia on way," the telegram read. "Will arrive Santa Fe ten o'clock Tuesday night. Gus Ernst."

"Who in the world is Sonia?" asked Ginny.

"For that matter," I said, thinking fast, "who is Gus Ernst?"

"I don't have any relatives named Sonia."

"And *I* don't have any named Gus Ernst."

"Probably a mistake," Ginny said. "Got us mixed up with some other Byrneses."

"I'll phone Western Union later," I said. "Let's not worry about it now. Whoever they are, they have till Tuesday to meet Sonia."

By Tuesday I was ready with a typical "working-late-at-the-office" alibi for not coming home at my regular time. "In fact," I said, "I may be working *very* late."

In my haste to buy Sonia, I had neglected to ask how old she was. I had taken it for granted that she would be a soft cuddly pup, a bit large of course, but manageable.

I was totally unprepared for the young horse-like creature that emerged from her crate on the freight-station platform.

The crate itself was about the size of a small bungalow. Sonia was as full grown, and strong, as a great Dane can be without passing out of the dog classification entirely. Furthermore, she was frightened and panicky. Two powerful freight handlers, who repeatedly yelled over her howling that dogs were usually crazy about them, had all they could do to get her into the car.

On the way home Sonia discovered she was most comfortable when squatting on the back seat, with her front legs and shoulders draped over the back of the front seat. During the ride her fears subsided, and Sonia began to show me the affectionate side of her nature by lathering me at frequent intervals with her tongue, which even when dry, must have weighed as much as a good-sized ham.

I arrived home exhausted, triumphant, and my face dripping wet from Sonia's kisses. As I turned the knob of the back door, she was seized with another fit of panic, and before I could stop her, lunged through the door and burst into the kitchen with the force of a hurricane. The door whipped back against the wall, smashing two empty milk bottles on the floor and knocking the curtain off an adjoining window.

A sudden feminine scream told me Ginny had discovered Sonia was no Western-Union mistake.

Sonia galloped into the dining room, hid under the table and expressed her feelings in a long series of howls that promptly woke the children, including the new baby. The frightened cries of the younger ones could be heard upstairs.

"Isn't she a beauty?" was all I could think of to say to my gasping wife. "Notice the authentic neck."

Ginny fought back hysteria.

We renamed Sonia the Good Samaritan, for what reason I can't recall, but even with that impressive title she didn't

work out too well. She proved to be the opposite of everything
a dog, particularly the noble Dane, is reputed to be. At least
a dozen times a day she would be taken with sudden and
inexplicable fits of fear, and go howling to some remote corner
of the property, often to remain there till nightfall, at which
time the older boys and myself would hunt her down with
flash lights, tie her and drag her home. A vet I talked to
diagnosed this as "a kind of personality problem."

Was she supposed to be good with children? She was
jealous of the younger ones and hid whenever they came too
close.

Was she supposed to be a watchdog? The only person she
ever guarded us against was the garbage man, a fact we first
discovered when we noticed that the garbage was beginning
to assume the proportions of an Indian-burial mound.

One winter day, when the heat was on in the house full
force, she wedged a paw between the coils of a hot radiator,
and stood off every attempt at rescue until in desperation I
dumped a pail of cold water on her head.

When she broke a bedroom window trying to get outside
to her boy friend, a roving-eyed Doberman, I decided I had
had enough "Tomorrow," I said firmly, "we advertise the
Good Samaritan for sale."

Two or three interested people came to look her over, but
as in the case of anything we try to get rid of, the sniffles
and swimming eyes of Ginny and the children discouraged
any serious selling. The would-be buyers, true dog lovers all,
unanimously agreed it would be a shame to take such a wonderful animal away from the youngsters.

"Nothing like a great Dane for kids," they all insisted.

"And such a beautiful dog," Ginny would chime in, through
her tears. "Just look at that adorable neck."

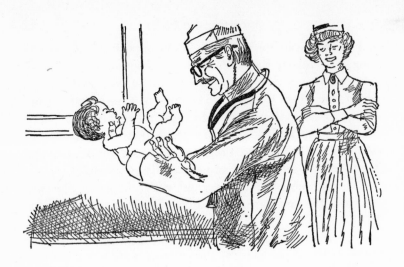

5 · Measles

The doctor finished his examination and sat back on the chair beside the bed. His expression was carefully non-committal. And that was a bad sign, because his expression, no matter how serious the ailment, usually says more plainly than words, "You're as sick as a dog, but we'll have you up in no time."

In the doorway Nina, Danielle and Peggy good-naturedly wriggled and nudged each other for the best vantage point without actually disobeying me by entering the room.

Mummy was sick, but there was nothing to worry about. Wasn't Dr. Richards here? Didn't he always make you get well? In fact, wasn't it *fun* having Dr. Richards call on you?

It was, and he always had a supply of lollypops to give the younger ones. And maybe the older ones, too, if they gave him a kiss.

"Well," said the doctor finally, his face unchanged, "you have the measles all right."

The girls giggled from the doorway. "Oh, Mummy, now you'll get lots of funny little spots."

"Of all ridiculous things!" said Ginny.

"They're German measles," said the doctor, as off-handedly as possible, but his eye was wary to see how much Ginny knew.

"German measles?" She frowned. "I remember reading somewhere. . . ."

"Well," I said, relieved. "Measles, eh?" Everybody got measles sooner or later, mostly sooner. A few days' discomfort, spots on the face and body, a sore throat. I too thought there was something rather comical about an adult catching a childhood disease like measles. "You'll look cute, dear," I said. "Red has always been your color."

The frown had slipped from Ginny's face, but the face was whiter than before. "Aren't German measles supposed to be bad for the baby?"

The doctor patted her hand. "You've been working pretty hard, I imagine," he said. "A few days in bed won't hurt you one bit."

"But the baby—"

"Don't you worry."

The girls and I followed Dr. Richards downstairs and into the living room. "You girls go back and keep your mother company," he said.

They were speechless. No lollypops?

"Go ahead now," he said, and they went.

"But shouldn't they stay away from her?" I asked. Won't *they* get the measles, too?"

"I hope they do," he said.

He took me by the arm and led me outside. We walked slowly toward his car. "Look," I said, beginning to wonder, "why so serious? After all—measles."

"There's something I have to tell you."

A chorus of yells rose from a cluster of honeysuckle bushes on the far side of the meadow. Kip and Dave were storming out of their bramble "fort" and charging an imaginary enemy. "Eeay!" they screamed. Wooden rifles in hand, they galloped the length of the meadow and back again. Their heads ducked behind the tall grass, and the bushes swallowed them up.

"She's six weeks along now, isn't that right?" Dr. Richards asked.

"You ought to know," I said, trying to shake off the feeling that this was not going to be the usual pleasant adieu. "But what's that got to do with measles?"

"German measles," the doctor corrected. *"Rubella.* We're learning a lot about it these days."

I waited.

"They're very hard on the baby, especially around this period in the mother's pregnancy."

"Measles? Measles hard on the baby? How do you mean?"

"I mean that the baby has less than a fifty-fifty chance of being born completely normal."

"My God!" The meadow seemed to tilt suddenly at an angle, as a projected scene on a motion-picture screen will jump where a portion of the film has been deleted and the remaining ends poorly rematched. Insignificant details of our surroundings—the robin's nest in the pine tree we were passing, the broken windowpane in the garage—became disproportionately conspicuous, as if flooded with a brilliant light. "Look at *us*," they seemed to say. "We're *real!*"

"It's not something we're just guessing at," the doctor went on. "Clinical observations of retarded children show too great an instance of German measles in the mother's pregnancy for guessing."

He laid his hand on my shoulder. "You see," he explained, trying to be kind when it was impossible to be anything but brutally frank, "the embryo suffers the disease, too. What makes it bad is that right now the brain, the heart, the eyes, ears and other organs are in their early formative stages. They're easily damaged."

The brain . . . "Less than a fifty-fifty chance?"

He nodded.

"But," I appealed, "isn't there *something* we can do?"

The chorus of yells rose once again from the honeysuckle hedge. "Charge!"

The doctor and I looked at each other for a long moment, and his eyes told me, yes, there *is* something you can do—but you won't do it.

"Keep in touch with me," he said abruptly, and stepped into his car.

I went back into the house and sought comfort in the sight of old, familiar objects: the table, stained by the Mercurochrome Peggy had spilled, the ragged cushion of the big chair which Danielle had scuffed with the heels of her new shoes, the dolls and doll clothes and toy cars that littered the floor under the piano, where the younger ones were always playing house.

And I thought, how many times during the next weeks and months will I try to find comfort in these things and feel only a kind of betrayal, as I feel it now.

"What did he say?" Ginny asked, knowing that a serious conversation had taken place.

"He said you have nothing to worry about," I lied.

"But I *know* German measles are dangerous for the baby."

"The doctor said when your health is generally good and you're strong—" I bluffed my way through a rambling, disconnected concert of assurances that fooled neither of us. But the closer communion of spirits that talking encouraged was what we both needed most. At last, with a gesture of her hand, as if brushing the whole business out of her mind, she said, "I *know* everything will be all right. I'm not even going to talk about it again."

A few days later she was well enough to get out of bed.

"I feel wonderful," she said bravely. "I *know* everything is going to be fine. My babies are all so healthy."

"You bet they are."

I handed her the morning paper, which Dave had just brought in from the back steps.

"I'll bet this baby will be the healthiest of them all," I said. I was even beginning to believe it myself.

Then suddenly from behind the newspaper came a gasp of shocked surprise.

"Oh, Tim," she cried, "listen to this!"

I hurried beside her. "New Findings Disclosed On German Measles," the headline read.

It was all there, the whole dismal parade of horrifying possibilities, from the weak eyes, the faulty hearing, to the damaged brain. Two university professors had devoted years to studying the connection between German measles in pregnant women and its pitiful manifestations in their children. The professors had done their work well, and the newspaper had faithfully reported every detail.

The next few days and nights were like the dreams of high fever, unreal and phantasmagoric, with only momentary openings into the world of reality, as we bent to the daily round of feeding and caring for the children.

There were fleeting images of faces sober with sympathy, and sounds of half-remembered voices: "I know what *I'd* do if I were you. . . . It could grow up to be a terrible burden on your other children. . . . After all, this is the twentieth century. . . . Nobody need know."

One image was clear . . . the memory of an old priest, tired with many years, sitting at his desk in the classroom, the spring breeze from the open window stirring the white locks of his great Ciceronian head, and his rich voice rolling on and on, as it had for years, filling the classroom with the rumbling phraseology of the moral law.

And I was listening. Seventeen years listening to eighty.

"We were created by God and no one but God has the right to take a human life, whether the life belong to a useless, tottering old fellow like myself (laughter) or a child in the womb."

To keep awake and show some interest (which would influence the Religion mark on your report card) you posed profound questions compounded of the most absurd improbables.

"Father—"

"Thomas?"

"But, Father, just suppose it is *certain* that a man is going to die, and suffer great agonies. And suppose his agonies make him curse God. Wouldn't it be better to take the old man's life and save him for Heaven, Father?"

"And wouldn't you care where you went yourself in that case, Thomas?"

Or—

"Father—"

"Yes, Thomas?"

"Father, just suppose it was certain that a woman who had a lot of children would die if she gave birth to her next child. Wouldn't it be better to take the child's life and save the mother so she could make sure her other children would lead good, clean lives?"

"Since when did we start preparing people for Heaven by committing murder, Thomas?"

Or suppose a child were to be born whose chances were less than fifty-fifty of being a normal human being.

Religion, we were told then, is man's greatest comfort. Certainly it was a comfortable subject to study in your seventeenth year when old men dying in agony, and mothers facing death in childbirth were creatures from a kind of academic never-never land. And the Commandments seemed so pat and precise, and so easy to understand. And old priests who never had to worry about children of their own marked your report card on the basis of your ability to memorize a certain number of questions and answers.

And then, suddenly, *you* were the "just suppose." The catechism became alive, blocking your path. And in a great breath-taking flash of understanding, you realized that all those questions and answers had been addressed directly to *you!*

We visited a young priest of whom Ginny and I were very fond. "Worries?" he said. "Do you think you can escape them entirely? Some women have the terrible worry of whether their husbands love them any more."

Ginny warmed me with one of her old smiles.

"Prayer is the only thing," he said. "Put the whole thing in the hands of God."

"We *will* pray," said Ginny fervently.

"I'll bet you will," he said. "In fact, I'll guarantee these will be the best prayers you've ever said in your whole lives."

Outside on the doorstep of the rectory, Ginny turned to me, her face alight. "Do you know what I'm going to do? I'm going to stop trying to hypnotize myself into thinking everything's fine. I'm going to try not to worry whether it's fine or not. I'm going to turn the remaining months of my pregnancy into a novena to St. Jude, the patron of hopeless cases! And not for any miracle, but for strength to take whatever comes."

It was the old warm house once more, warm with the old familiar objects, the table, the ragged cushion of the big chair, the toys scattered under the piano. They welcomed us home.

"There's a window in the delivery-room door," the nurse said. "If you want to watch—"

I admire the courage of the expectant father who can witness the delivery of his child. But it is a courage I would rather not have to call upon.

"Thanks," I said. "But I'll wait in the hall."

My own feelings at the moment seemed immensely unimportant compared to the drama that was unfolding in the delivery room, and which Ginny related afterwards in every unforgotten detail.

Near the end the obstetrician had bent over her, his voice

muffled by the gauze mask. "I may give you a whiff of gas," he said.

"You won't have to," Ginny whispered between contractions. "The spinal will be enough."

He had already given her a spinal anesthetic in preference to others, because he felt it would be easiest on the baby.

"Well," he said, "if I do give you gas, I want you to take it."

She knew why he wanted her to take it. The doctor, she was sure, had not made a novena to St. Jude on this particular case. If things went terribly wrong, it would be better if she didn't see. The gas would do the trick.

"Bear down, Ginny," he said.

The anesthetist hovered like a guardian angel about her head. They talked in whispers. They all knew.

The minutes ticked by. Even the spinal anesthetic could not block off all the pain, which flooded her body in deep, spasmodic rushes.

"The head is down," someone said.

The anesthetist was on her feet, the gas mask poised with its blessed promise of sleep.

Then at last there was a final burst of pain, and suddenly Ginny had room to breathe, fast and deep, the breathing of exhaustion.

She lifted her head. The gas mask moved to within inches of her face. But the baby was already in the doctor's hands— a big, round, red, bawling baby, a beautiful baby, "the best," he insisted later, "of them all!" And a boy.

The doctor turned him over, peering at him closely. Then he said what other doctors, after careful examinations, were soon to repeat, "He's a beauty."

The anesthetist sighed, and set down the mask.

"His name," said Ginny humbly, "is Thomas Jude!"

6 · Woman Wanted

"Woman wanted," the ad read, "to take care of easily managed children during day while mother is in hospital. Pleasant home surroundings."

"*That* ought to bring results," I said to Ginny, as I folded the paper. "Notice the clever wording. Nothing about how *many* easily managed children. That will come after I've completely sold them on the fresh air and sunshine."

"But when you *do* tell them—"

"Leave it to me."

In about three weeks Ginny would deliver our eighth, and we were face to face with the old problem of how to take care of the others during their mother's stay in the hospital.

Naturally we had faced this little puzzler often. The first

birth, of course, gave us no worry in that respect at all. The only one left home was myself—and not for long. Parents, neighbors, even friends I hadn't heard from for years, were convinced I needed special feeding during this trying period, and deluged me with invitations to breakfast, lunch, dinner and midnight snacks. It took some time to convince Ginny my sudden gain in weight was *not* proof that I thrived better on other people's cooking. It was just that there were too many other people.

With three, four, and five—even six—kids, the problem was still manageable. There were always enough relatives willing to come in and run the house, at least in shifts, or to distribute the children among their households.

But with seven to be guided through a motherless week, I had to admit I was stuck. The children had reached a stage where they seemed to prefer family unity to life itself. They flatly refused to be divided up among the relatives. The relatives, in turn, with an eye to their own family unity, just as flatly refused to take the children in any but small, digestible doses.

A kindly neighbor offered one solution. She insisted her twelve-year-old Mary Josephine was perfectly qualified to come in and run the house and children during the day because, although only twelve, "she has the sense of a twenty one year old." Besides, it was vacation time, and a job would keep her out of mischief.

This proposal Ginny turned down for two reasons. She had her doubts about any twelve year old (particularly Mary Josephine) possessing the sense of twenty-one, and if keeping her out of mischief was the object, a house with seven mischief-makers of its own, was hardly the place to do it.

Several of the neighbors offered to help, but Ginny refused to impose on their kindness. "It's not *their* fault I'm having a baby," she said.

That seemed to put it squarely up to me. "Let's be sensible about this," I said, "and hire professional help. No more fuss or worrying. There must be hundreds of women looking for work like this." And so I wrote the ad.

Of the hundreds of women looking for work like this about a dozen answered the ad, but a dozen was enough. The over-the-phone interviews followed pretty much the same pattern.

"Hello? This the party that advertised for a woman to mind the kids?"

"Why, yes. Now let me tell you a little—"

"How many kids y'got?"

"Well, as I was about to say—"

"I said how many kids y'got?"

"What?"

"Look, mister, the ad says *kids*. All I wanna know is how many!"

"Well, there are seven at home, and—"

The response from the other end was usually an explosion of wild and bitter laughter. "Seven! My God! That's more than I got myself! Your poor wife!" Or they would simply hang up without saying a word. I came to appreciate this latter response best of all.

"But don't worry," I consoled Ginny one evening. "We still have two weeks before you're due. We'll find somebody in that time. . . . Why, what's the matter, dear?"

Her features had set in the old familiar attitude of sudden watchfulness, as if she were listening to catch the far-away crying of one of the children.

"I had a pain," she said.

Mary Josephine was a small, spindly girl, whose thin, freckled features were dwarfed by an enormous shock of red hair and a yellow hair bow that flapped when she moved like the wings of a tired sea gull. When I arrived home from the hospital—and the birth of Mary Johanna—late next morning, she was playing on the floor with the younger children. Kip, who was the same age as Mary Josephine, was watching television in high disdain for my reliance on someone no older than he was. But I felt, or at least hoped, that this particular someone would not glue herself to the television set and remain there even if the house were to burn down, as I was convinced Kip would do.

"I'm sure happy you were able to come," I told her.

"Ma was glad you called," she answered without looking up. "Ma says you'd never get anybody but a crazy woman to stay with so many kids."

When I asked her if she'd keep a close eye on the babies, she assured me, "We'll have a lot of fun."

Obviously, she was already having a lot of fun. Stretched out flat on her stomach, surrounded by the others, who viewed her with awe, she was playing with David's electric train.

"Pa would never get me an electric train," she said. "Pa says they're not for girls. I love them. Whoo-whoo! The train is coming into the station right now!"

I said, "Would it be too much of a job to wash the breakfast dishes and sort of clean up the kitchen?"

"I'd rather watch the kids," said Mary Josephine. "Soapy water gives me a rash. I have to use a special cream when I wash myself. The train is pulling out of the station now. Whoo-whoo!"

I told the children I had to go to the office for a while, but that I'd be home early, and kissed them all good-by. Automatically, Mary Josephine stood up to be kissed, too.

I pulled the front door after me slowly. Did I dare leave this bunch? She must be a level-headed kid, I thought; her mother said so.

"The train is going through a mountain, pretend," came the voice of Mary Josephine. "Whoo-whoo!"

I went back into the house. The office would have to wait.

Later that morning, the sound of the telephone came through the whining of the vacuum cleaner.

"How are you making out, Tom?" It was the voice of Ginny's mother.

"Not bad," I said, reaching over with my foot to snap off the vacuum cleaner. "Got my dusting finished, the dishes washed, and the kitchen pretty straight. Next job is their lunch."

"Isn't the girl doing *anything?*"

"Oh, sure. She found some extra track in the basement, and they've stretched the railroad into the dining room now."

"The train is stranded in the desert," shouted Mary Josephine. "The passengers are dying of thirst!"

"Ye-ay!" the children hollered.

"Good heavens," said my mother-in-law, "I can hear them! Poor Tom." There was the sound of a deep resolute breath. Common sense was about to be thrown to the winds. "Tom, there's only one thing to do. You pack them all up and bring them into Chicago."

"But there won't be room!" Her apartment had definitely not been planned to accommodate seven children in addition to her own husband and two unmarried daughters.

"We'll *make* room—at least until you find somebody. The

girls can sleep in my bed, I can go on the couch, and—of *course* there'll be room. I have it all figured out. Now don't waste a minute. Hurry!" There was the kind of note in her voice that must have been in Farragut's when he said, "Damn the torpedoes! Full speed ahead!" It meant plainly, "You can argue till doomsday, but it won't do you any good."

"We'll be there as soon as we can," I said.

Mary Josephine was delighted at the prospect of a trip into Chicago.

"You don't understand, Mary Josephine," I said patiently. "Just *my* kids are going. You're going home."

"Can't," said Mary Josephine.

"Why not?"

"My mother doesn't get home from work till six o'clock. I can't get in the house."

"I didn't know your mother worked."

"She helps out at Doolittle's every Wednesday. Mrs. Doolittle goes into Chicago every Wednesday for ceramics. Is she ever good!"

I thought of suggesting that Mary Josephine play around outside until her mother arrived, but it occurred to me that it would be quite in character if she wandered away and got kidnapped or broke an arm or leg while climbing a tree ten blocks from home. After all, I reminded myself, my sense of responsibility growing weightier every second, you *are* accountable for her in a way. I wasn't quite sure what the "way" was, but I felt it was not of minor proportions.

"Oh, Daddy," Nina and Danielle pleaded, "*please* let her come!"

"I could watch the kids," said Mary Josephine.

I had a choice of two procedures. On the one hand I could wait until her mother came home, deliver Mary Josephine, come back, feed the children, pack them into the car and take them to Chicago. That would mean messing up the kitchen again, washing babies and dishes, and travelling with the children dog tired, cranky and half of them asleep. Or I could leave now with all of them and bring Mary Josephine back home after the others had been safely deposited with Ginny's mother.

"Please, *please*, Daddy, take her with us!" squealed the girls.

Ginny's mother paled a little at the sight of the extra visitor, but recovered quickly when I explained the situation.

"I'm glad you're here early," she said, "before Daddy got home."

I lifted a tired eyebrow.

"It will be so much easier to make him understand with the children already here," she went on.

"You mean he doesn't *know?*"

There must have been moments when even Farragut worried about the torpedoes. "Why don't you mix yourself a drink?" she suggested.

I mixed a good stiff one.

"I'd better be going now," I said, after downing the drink in one gulp. "Mary Josephine is expected home."

"Please, *please* let her stay," the girls bellowed.

Danielle, blonde, peppery, wrapped her arms around my legs to add emphasis to her pleas. Nina, dark, demure, squeezed my arm and flashed me the wide-eyed smile she had used so successfully on other occasions. Kip and Dave were already slumped in the nearest chairs and obviously didn't care *who* stayed. The younger ones were busily exploring the other rooms of the apartment.

But I can be tough when the occasion demands. I gripped Mary Josephine firmly by the hand.

"Good-by," I said to the children, "be good, and do everything Grandma says." Then I added as an afterthought, "Or I'll knock your blocks off."

Ginny's folks lived on the top floor of an apartment building served by an automatic elevator. Even before I pressed the button that would bring the car up from below, a grinding, humming noise told me the car was already on its way, probably with a passenger.

The door slid open and my father-in-law stepped out, a "hard day at the office" written plainly on his face.

"Well," he said wearily, "this *is* a surprise."

You don't know the half of it, I thought, pushing Mary Josephine into the car.

"Won't you stay and have a drink?" he asked cordially.

"Can't," I stuttered. "T-tight schedule. Ginny's expecting me."

The car door slid between us, screening off his puzzled expression.

"How are the children?" I heard him call.

"Fine!" I shouted back. "Oh, Lord," I thought, "how soon he'll find out!"

Early the next morning Ginny's mother called to ask if I had located anybody to stay with the children.

I lied that I had.

"That's good," she said, understandably relieved. "My plans for sleeping everybody last night didn't include Daddy. He slept sitting up."

"Don't worry," I said weakly, "everything's under control."

"I hope it's not Mary Josephine again. Frankly, I think she's a little too young."

"Oh, no," I continued to lie. "It's someone *much* older."

I didn't see any point in telling her that Mary Josephine's mother had just called to say her daughter couldn't make it today. She was sick, it seemed, and they thought she was coming down with whooping cough.

But I need not have worried about the help problem. For Mary Josephine's mother, without a word to me, had alerted the neighborhood to my plight. Within half an hour "Operation-save-the-Byrneses" was in full swing. A hearty female voice soon phoned me to give me the time schedule for the various maneuvers. Mrs. Ryan would come in at nine to wash the breakfast dishes. She would be relieved at a quarter of eleven by Mrs. Casperi, who would tidy up the house and see things through until two-thirty, at which time there would be an unavoidable ten-minute gap between Mrs. Casperi's departure and the arrival of Mrs. Tumsett, who would leave forty-five minutes later to pick up Mrs. Caldwell, who would run things until a little after five, at which time she would be relieved by Mrs. Connors, who would depart at six, providing Mrs. Meers' sister Ethyl could catch a train from town, where she had been shopping, in time to feed her own family and then get over to our house and supervise us while we had dinner. With difficulty I convinced my caller that I was able to put the children to bed myself.

With minor variations, this was the daily schedule right up to the time of Ginny's return. I was very grateful for the neighbors' help but rather unprepared for some of its consequences. I began receiving strange phone calls in the evening. "This is Mr. Gutlik, of Gutlik's Grocery. Just want to thank

you for finally giving us your business, Mr. Byrnes. Been trying to serve you for a long time, remember? Thanks a lot."
Or "This is Central Market, Mr. Byrnes. Called to get your
order this morning and a strange woman said you're trading
at Gutlik's now. If there's anything wrong—"

Or a neighbor, formerly friendly, would say, "Look here,
Byrnes, our kids have played together for a long time. What's
the idea of sending my Margery home this afternoon with
instructions not to come back?"

Or "This is Joe Marsh. I thought you wanted me to fix that
tile in the septic tank."

"Sure, Joe, that's what I said."

"Well, this afternoon I get over there with forty bucks
worth of materials and some dame says she's sure you wanna
get a lot of estimates first."

But then at last, Ginny came home. The Central Market
was once more delivering our groceries, our kids were playing
happily with Margery, and Joe Marsh fixed the tile in the
septic tank. Also, my clean shirts, sox and handkerchiefs
were again to be found in their usual places.

And as I told myself, it's better for the kids to have the
whooping cough when they're young and get it over with.

7 · A Fine Father I Am!

By the time Gael Marie, our ninth baby, was on the way, I had fully determined there would be no more crises over who would take care of the others during Ginny's absence. I would take care of them myself.

At first the idea was nothing more than a wish. "I wish I could give my kids more of the fatherly companionship they need."

Usually these fits of paternal self-reproach occur at comfortable periods when there isn't much I can do about them, as when I'm hundreds of miles away on a business trip. But this time the feeling struck me right at home, and persisted.

I've got to spend more time with my kids, I kept thinking. I see them for a few minutes in the morning, just long enough to tell them to behave themselves during the day, as if they were in a perpetual state of probation. I come home late in the evening; I'm tired; they're tired; we get on each other's nerves; all I can think of saying is, "Be quiet," or "It's time to go to bed now."

Hang it all, I thought, they're growing up, and I don't even know them. They start out as helpless, hungry, howling infants, all of them looking and acting pretty much alike.

Then one day something is said, something done, that makes you look at them closely and you see them as individuals with traits and characters as distinct as the book titles in your library.

Here is Kip, who once looked and acted pretty much like David, or any other new-born baby, looking and acting now like nobody but himself, tall, rangy, deliberate, a daydreamer and natural athlete, who with equal facility can calm a restless horse or keep a baby amused by dangling the fingers of his big hands over the side of the crib.

And here is David, quick, restless, protective of the others, once distractingly mischievous, now proud of whatever responsibilities you give him.

And dark-eyed, dark-haired Nina, with her passion for dancing and memorizing poetry. And blonde Danielle, who makes you think of firecrackers when she isn't singing and making you think of violins. And Peggy, as yet quiet and shy, but with sparkling eyes that make you wonder what changes the next few years will bring, if you stop long enough to wonder.

And pudgy, apple-cheeked Tommy, the "prizefighter," as his brothers call him; and bubbling Tony, who recites grace before meals and the latest TV commercial with the same fervor. And Mary-Jo, who talked earlier than the rest, and much more often.

What enormous transformations have taken place before my eyes. And were my eyes always open? How much have I helped or hindered?

But when Ginny goes to the hospital and I have eight motherless mites depending on me alone, what better opportunity to make up for lost time? I would simply tell the office I was taking my vacation.

When I first outlined the plan, a few weeks before the baby arrived, Ginny foresaw several problems.

"Just feeding them," she said. "What a job *that* is."

"I'm young yet," I said. "And strong."

"And there'll be the laundry. You'll have to send part of it out and do the baby's things in the automatic."

"The older ones will help."

"And ordering groceries, and cleaning house. No, darling, I *couldn't* let you."

I knew I had won. Whenever Ginny says, "I couldn't let you," it means she is on the verge of throwing the whole job, whatever it is, squarely in my lap.

"Don't worry," I said easily. "I'll have the best fun I've had in years. All *you* have to do is tell our friends this is going to be *my* show."

She frowned. "Oh," she said, shaking her head. "If *I* told them, they'd think I didn't want them around. But if *you* told them . . ." The sentence trailed off in a smile of complete confidence.

I handled the job of telling by forgetting all about it, an oversight that may be classified generally as a mistake.

I realized this the day Gael Marie was born. I arrived home

late in the afternoon to find Nina, Danielle and Peggy trying to get our great Dane, The Good Samaritan, away from the door of the downstairs bathroom.

From three different versions of what was happening I managed to extract two pieces of seemingly unrelated information, namely, that The Good Samaritan had been holding down this particular spot for more than fifteen minutes, and that she didn't like Mrs. Meers' sister Ethyl.

"What has Mrs. Meers' sister Ethyl got to do with it?" I asked.

"She's in here," Nina said, pointing to the bathroom door.

"And she's awful sad, too," Danielle added.

The sound of soft weeping from the other side of the door verified the fact that Mrs. Meers' sister Ethyl was indeed sad.

"Where are those boys?" I demanded angrily, as I propelled The Good Samaritan down the basement stairs and slammed the door after her.

"They're over at Mason's farm, helping him cut logs," Nina supplied.

I had forgotten that at this same after-school hour every day the older boys could be counted on to be out working anywhere but on their own place.

There're going to be some changes around here," I muttered.

Through the door I called an apology to Mrs. Meers' sister Ethyl. "I'm awfully sorry this happened. I never dreamed that mutt would do a thing like that."

The only answer was more sobs.

"It's safe to come out now," I repeated. "The dog's in the basement." The sobbing continued.

"I got an A in spelling today," Nina filled in.

"And the O'Malley boys said their father is going to speak to you about Peggy."

"Why?"

"Because she stuffed their mail box full of rotten apples."

"You shouldn't do such things," I remarked absently to Peggy, my attention still on the bathroom. Then I remembered the O'Malley house was fully two miles away. "What were you doing that far from home?" I demanded.

"She ran away," Danielle answered.

"And Danielle went with her," Nina said.

"I just went so I could see where she was going," Danielle defended herself.

"The two of you alone on that road!" I exploded.

The bathroom door swung open. "I refuse to take the blame for that," said Ethyl, dabbing her tear-stained face with a tiny ball of a handkerchief. "I can't be two places at once. I was upstairs making the beds, and all of a sudden Peggy was gone. And then that brute of a dog got loose from the basement and cornered me in the bathroom, and what could I do?"

At this moment she was having all she could do to keep on being angry. A fluffy dumpling of a woman, with dimpled cheeks and a head full of tight ringlets, she had as little aptitude as a kewpie doll for looking indignant.

"You should have called me when Ginny left," she said accusingly. "You poor man! What a time you must be having."

"Not at all," I protested. "Everything's dandy."

"Just think," she ignored me, "I would never have known if I hadn't spied the children waiting for the bus this morning." At this point she shooed the girls out of the kitchen.

"You'd never have known what?" I asked cooperatively.

"That Ginny wasn't home. Oh, I'm not criticizing you,

you understand. But blue jeans—and old ones with the knees out!"

The devil, I thought, were the boys wearing their old blue jeans?

"You couldn't be expected to know it," Ethyl went on, "but the school frowns on girls wearing blue jeans."

"On *what* wearing blue jeans?"

"Danielle was wearing them," said Ethyl.

I tried to recall what Danielle looked like as she left, but all I could remember was a blonde head tilted upward to be kissed good-by.

"And the boys' shoes. I know you couldn't have seen them leave or you'd never have let them go with all that mud on their shoes."

It wasn't mud, I thought glumly. It was fresh cow manure from Mason's barn.

"And poor little Nina. How lonesome she must feel."

What was wrong with Nina, I wondered. Then I recalled that her usual morning question, "What dress shall I wear?" —a question that used to try the patience of Ginny—had not been asked this morning. Nina had evidently decided she was at last old enough to answer that problem herself, and had done so by wearing yesterday's wrinkled and well-spotted garment.

"Oh, Lord," I groaned, in spite of myself.

"Now don't you worry," Ethyl reassured me. "We're not going to let you go all to pieces just because you wife's not home." She led me over to the stove, loaded with simmering pans. "There'll be cauliflower and spinach and potatoes, and I made some gravy for that cold lamb in the refrigerator, so I guess you'll have enough. I can't stay," she added regretfully, "Bimmy is expecting me home. But he'll drive me back so I can clean up the dishes afterwards. Incidentally, the baby's been fed."

I tried to protest that a return trip wasn't necessary, but she smothered me under a gale of laughter and disappeared out the kitchen door in a blustery aura of good will toward men.

When the children settled down to the table, they made the shocking discovery that the meal was composed almost entirely of inedibles. "Cauliflower!" one of them shouted, as if it were a bowl of poison ivy. "Spinach!" cried another. "Daddy," they wailed, "we can't eat *this!*"

"You'll eat it or go right to bed! There are kids in this world who'd give their right arm for a bowl of cauliflower. It—it builds muscles," I added lamely. The girls in particular were unimpressed.

It was not a happy mealtime. The children ate slowly, staring rebelliously at the table, and moving their jaws as slowly as they could. My efforts to start a conversation drew only monosyllabic answers.

David, as usual when under pressure, developed a giggling fit. Danielle, his counterpart in temperament, giggled back, and as a side interest began to pinch Peggy under the table. Peggy spilled her glass of milk trying to retaliate. The confusion mounted, so did the giggles.

Half an hour later, their plates still full, I noticed for the first time that they had been filling up surreptitiously on bread and butter.

I began to lose my temper. Peggy, as always, took my reprimands as a disavowal of love, and left the table in a flood of tears. David's giggling got worse. Kip began to snicker, then laugh. Never, I thought, was there this trouble with Ginny around. What's the matter with *me?*

"All right," I said firmly, "leave the table. Go outside or do anything you want to do." They slipped away like salmon eluding a net. "But be careful!" I yelled in a last attempt at maintaining authority.

A fine father I am, I thought. What a big kick the kids must get out of being with *me!* They almost fell over each other getting away from the table. Besides, I thought irrelevantly, I've wasted all this food.

A scratching at the basement door, however, suggested an answer to the waste problem. The Good Samaritan. I scraped the plates and bowls of food into the battered old stewing kettle that was The Good Samaritan's feeding dish, placed it outside the kitchen door at the foot of the steps, released the dog and closed the door on that particular problem.

I wandered disconsolately into the front room and sought comfort in the view from the big bay window. Under one of the oak trees on the front lawn, the children stood clustered together in a mournful little group like one of the Lost Tribes. Kip was absently picking pieces of bark off the tree with his thumbnail, and the rest were watching him in wordless dejection. Poor kids, I said to myself, they miss their mother.

I rapped smartly on the windowpane, smiled a big smile I hoped would be distinguishable in the half-dark, and beckoned them to come in.

"Aw," Kip called, "do we have to come in now?"

I nodded my head vigorously and tried to look as if great things were in store. Reluctantly, they moved across the lawn, picking up an occasional acorn to examine it on the way.

"Kids," I said, when they filed into the living room. "Whatsay we start a big fire and play a game or something?" Their eyes showed signs of returning life. "Okay," David said, with an inflection that meant, "Now you're getting somewhere."

Seated on the floor before the fire, the girls snuggled close. Peggy, her thumb in her mouth, rested her head on my lap. I remembered having read somewhere that sucking the thumb was bad for teeth alignment, and I gently pulled her hand away. Then I remembered having read somewhere else that sucking the thumb didn't matter, and, as gently, placed her thumb back in her mouth. "Sank you, Dadda," Peggy murmured in the special baby talk she reserved for tender occasions.

"Suppose," I said, leaning back against a chair arm, "I tell you a story."

"Yeee-ay!" they cried.

"But first," Kip interposed, "could we have something to eat? I'm hungry." He said it without the slightest feeling of guilt at having by-passed his dinner.

One or two of the others said they were hungry too, so, reluctantly, but delighted at the restored trust of my children, I led them out to the kitchen, where I made fried-egg sandwiches, garnished with dill pickles and great splashes of hot relish.

"This is more like it," said David.

They had just seated themselves again around the fire, with their sandwiches and glasses of milk, when the wheezing of an ancient car in the driveway announced Ethyl's return. Panicky, I shooed them upstairs with their second dinner. "Listen now," I panted, "you mustn't let Ethyl know you're eating again."

"Why?" asked Nina, as the front doorbell rang.

"Because she'd think you didn't like *her* food, see? And she'd feel awful. Now eat everything up as fast as you can and then climb into bed. As soon as she goes, I'll come up and say good-night."

"Yoo-hoo!" Ethyl was calling from below, having let herself in. "Anybody home?"

"Now remember!" I gave the children a final warning, as I started downstairs.

"This is Bimmy," Ethyl said, urging her husband to extend his hand. "Bimmy, meet Mr. Byrnes, the man I was telling you about."

Bimmy, a blond giant, favored me with a man-to-man smile, big enough to accommodate a watermelon, and shook my hand with the grip and gracefulness of a hydraulic press.

"I've heard a lot aboutcha," beamed Bimmy.

"He's simply dying to see the children," said Ethyl. "Let's go up." She regarded the house with the easy familiarity of a woman who just a few hours before has made up the beds and cooked the dinner.

"If it's all the same to you," I said in a sweat, "we'd better leave them alone. You see," I swallowed desperately, "they're saying their prayers."

"Oh, sure," said Bimmy. "In that case—"

"The dears!" squealed Ethyl. "And we have to miss that!"

"Well, I'll tell you," I said, with a silent prayer of my own, "I'm having trouble getting 'em to stay on their knees, and if we interrupt them now—" I winked portentiously to indicate that all the radiators in the house would explode if the children got off their knees. I led Bimmy into the living room. Ethyl, slightly puzzled, disappeared into the kitchen.

From behind clouds of cigar smoke, Bimmy launched into a good-natured recital of the vicissitudes of the cartage business. With the ease of a man who knows his subject well, he discoursed at length on everything from the relative merits of fuel pumps to the dangers of driving semi-trailers down steep slopes in icy weather.

At times I cocked a restless ear to catch any signs of revolt from upstairs, but there was no sound in the house except the exuberant splashing of dish water in the kitchen and the steady drone of Bimmy's voice.

"How about seeing the kids now?" Bimmy suggested at one point, but by then I was ready for him.

"Tell you what," I said. "You folks will have to come back some other evening when they're awake. If we woke them up now I'd be all evening getting them back to sleep. You know how kids need sleep," I added.

"Oh, sure," said the agreeable Bimmy.

A little before midnight, after Ethyl had brewed coffee and made ham sandwiches for the three of us, she and her husband got up to go. As proof of their democratic good fellowship—which Bimmy swore was foursquare and resting on solid rock—they insisted on leaving via the kitchen door.

At the bottom of the steps, Ethyl stopped in her tracks.

"Go ahead, dear," said Bimmy, nudging her.

She continued to stare as if mesmerized by some object half-hidden in the shadows at her feet.

"What's wrong?" I asked.

Ethyl pointed numbly to The Good Samaritan's battered old stewing kettle, still holding, I noted with a tremor, the greater part of Ethyl's home cooking.

"I'll be damned," I stammered feebly. "How in the world did *that* get there?"

"I'm sure I don't know," said Ethyl, in the tone of a primeval glacier slicing through solid rock. "I'm *sure* I don't know."

I was still standing on the steps when Bimmy's ancient Buick, with a series of defiant backfires, rolled out of the driveway.

Upstairs the children were sleeping soundly, fully dressed, on top of the bedspreads, the empty milk glasses and sandwich plates beside them on the floor. What a wretched evening they've had, I thought guiltily. Tomorrow has to be a lot better.

I removed their shoes and outer clothing, and covered them up warmly. Through it all they slept soundly—except Nina, the warm, motherly one, who came to long enough to murmur, "Wasn't it fun, *everybody* together in front of the fire?"

In the morning Ethyl called up as if nothing had happened and told me not to worry. She wasn't going to let me go all to pieces just because my wife wasn't home.

8 · What Every Father Should Know

"The second baby is always easier than the first." This ranks high among the more popular hallucinations about child bearing. Apparently the more babies you have, the less painful they become, until around the ninth or tenth the mother's sensations are ones of pure ravishment.

While untrue in the case of the mother, this "the-more-the-merrier" attitude is even less appropriate where the father is concerned.

Once a man has become a parent, he immediately earns a kind of "security clearance" which entitles him to all the horror stories on childbirth the old hands can throw his way. The old hands, or experts, may range from the woman in the room next to your wife to the fellow delivering Worcestershire sauce to Gutlik's Grocery the day you're telling Mr. Gutlik about the latest arrival.

The embryo father first comes to grips with this higher authority shortly after the first baby is born. He begins to hear, as part of the congratulatory messages, what a lucky fellow he was that his child had such a *normal* birth. He is soon trembling at the thought of all the things that could have gone wrong. "Like poor Mrs. So-and-so," they'll say. "Everything going along just fine—just *fine*—when what d'you think happens? The baby is born facing backwards."

By the time his second is on the way, the average father is a walking lexicon of horror stories. He will be told, however, not to worry (the second is always easier, etc.). But he knows better. What about Mrs. What's-her-name's baby who was born with its brains in its abdomen—and just when they thought everything was going along just fine?

Heaven help the expectant father if the hospital waiting room is anywhere near a solarium or reading room or other gathering place of the ambulatory patients. I spent time in one such room that was located next to the showers. The showers could hold only a few bathers at a time, so the overflow, tiring one by one of standing in the hall, smiled their way to the chair- and couch-arms opposite me. So my wife was having a baby! And her ninth! "You're kidding. Well, isn't that wonderful. And your wife is fine? Well, aren't you lucky! Here I've had only two children and my uterus is tipped in six different directions. The doctor just can't *imagine!*"

I never before had such a thorough briefing in the number and variety of female complaints. Apparently each and every female organ exists for the prime purpose of making the mother's stay on earth as short and painful as possible. Portions of her anatomy, interior and exterior, that I had hitherto considered subjects only for text books or medical consultations, were referred to as freely, and lugubriously, as if they were names of famous catastrophes of history.

I began to perspire. Maybe it *was* time for our luck to change. Eight kids, and all they seemed to do to Ginny was improve her figure. This good fortune couldn't last. When I thought of what the woman in the green kimono had just said—

"Congratulations," said a nurse, coming in. "Your wife has a wonderful eight-pound baby girl."

The experts squealed in unison.

"How is my wife?" I gasped. "Is everything all right?"

Taken back by the intensity of my concern, the nurse was more than reassuring. "Everything is just fine. Now don't you worry. It was a very easy birth."

A shadow rolled past the doorway. From one end of the mountain of sheets and blankets, Ginny's face, bright with the joyous news, was turned toward me. She lifted a hand and waved.

"Did you see that?" one of the women exclaimed.

"She actually waved!"

"Oh, well," sighed another. "Nine babies—what do you expect?"

Next to the horror stories in their unsettling effect on the father, is the flood of advice received from professional and non-professional alike.

The greatest authority on raising the children, of course, is the father's mother, the extent of whose influence depends on how soon the daughter-in-law catches on. Ginny caught on one June afternoon a few months after the birth of Kip, our first. She had left the baby with me while she went out shopping. She returned to find him bundled up warmly enough to face a blizzard.

"What in the world is the matter?" she gasped.

"Shhh," I whispered. "Mother dropped in while you were out. She's in the kitchen making a cup of tea."

"Your mother did this?"

I nodded, and fervently wished I had followed an earlier inclination to be a monk.

"What in the world is she trying to do," asked Ginny, peeling the baby's stockings off, "smother the child?"

"That you, Ginny?" my mother called from the kitchen.

"The baby's a little too hot," I answered, trying to ease up to the crisis as gently as possible. "We're taking a few things off."

"Oh, no, you *mustn't* do that," said mother, hurrying into the room. "It's too drafty with those windows open." She stopped in her tracks when she saw the act had been accomplished.

The two mothers faced each other.

"I don't want him to wear stockings on a warm day like this," Ginny said firmly.

Mother readied her big ammunition. "Old Dr. Henry always said—" she began.

"I don't care *what* Dr. Henry always said," retorted Ginny, a little tired of hearing what he always said. "*My* baby doctor says stockings are unnecessary in weather like this."

Here was high treason. Old Dr. Henry, made more infallible than ever by his death ten years before, had been the beginning and end of medicine for my mother. As far as she was concerned, healing was finished as a science the day the old doctor passed away.

"Oh," breathed my mother, "so stockings are unnecessary? Well, your husband was raised with stockings and they don't seem to have hurt him one bit. In fact he can thank his baby stockings that he doesn't have rheumatism today. Old Dr. Henry—"

But she caught herself in time. "All right," she said finally, "it's your baby, of course, and you can raise him as you wish. But you mustn't be above taking a little advice now and then."

At first we regarded the published advice of the child-guidance experts as highly as we did the sulpha drugs. We gave thanks that they had arrived in time to save our kids from who knows what awful ends. But as our children multiplied, we found it more and more difficult to follow these voices of experience.

"Is Toilet Training A Problem In Your Family?" the arresting headline would ask. If it wasn't, it soon became one after we read the article. "Be sure to bring your child to the bathroom at regular periods each day," the writer would say. This procedure turned out to be a direct violation of the wishes of the kids. They resented being hauled to the toilet except at the latest necessary moment. The more individual of them still insisted on announcing their needs by rushing up at unexpected moments, even in the presence of guests, shouting, "Seat, Mummy, seat!" Whereupon Ginny or myself would scoop them up and hurry them off, hoping we'd make it in time. In the season of winter clothing, this system, or lack of it, could be pretty unnerving for someone without lightning fingers or a strong gambling instinct.

"Are Your Children Hard To Please At Table?" was another challenge that spoiled many a mealtime for us. To begin with, we were told, the chairs must be comfortable. Secondly, don't season the food heavily lest it dull delicate young appetites.

How the children knew whether the chairs were comfortable or not I could never figure out; for they perched on the very edges or sat with one leg, or both, doubled up under them. As for seasoning, the most attractive part of every meal seemed to be the salt and pepper.

There was one bit of advice, however, that I thought unique and well worth a good try. "Do You Talk To Your Children?" the writer asked. "Are you training them in the art of conversation, or are you simply letting them wander in the conversational meadows like lost sheep?" No need to hesitate on that one. We were letting them wander all right, although more like stampeding elephants than lost sheep.

The thing to do, the article said, is make up a list of topics to talk about, say, at dinnertime, then bring the list to the table with you and let it guide you from one informative subject to the other. If the talk is slow in getting started, the wise parent will know enough to get things going with a provocative question or two.

This sounded sensible, so one night I came to the table with a list of subjects I was sure would put an end to the aimless chatter that usually ebbed and flowed all around me.

For a while, I let the children do their own talking, just to get them warmed up. I listened without protest to the news that Nina was immune to poison ivy (so *she* thought), that Tony had fallen downstairs, that the cat had devoured two mice at one sitting, and so on through the soup.

Then I asked the first planned question, a neat lead-in, I thought, to a lively discussion on civic government. "Who," I said, "do you think paid for our town's new fire engine?"

There was a moment's amazed silence. Then Nina shouted, "Daddy! You *did?*"

"No," I protested, annoyed, "of course not. How could *I* afford a fire engine?"

"But you said—"

"I merely asked."

"Tony's filling up on bread and butter," said Danielle, the table watchdog. "He won't eat his peas."

"About this fire engine—" I began again.

"I'll ask Mr. Martin," said Kip. "He'll know."

Finally I tried another tack. "I'll bet not one of you know the name of our mayor."

David looked thoughtful. "I didn't think we had a mayor; I thought we had a village board and a president."

The table rocked with laughter. "Oh, *Daddy!*" they cried.

"Dear," said Ginny, covering my retreat, "why don't we just *listen?*"

I have never read an article entitled, "Do You Listen To Your Children?" But some day I hope to get around to writing one.

"I wonder," Nina pondered after a while, "what it would be like if wood kept right on growing after it was cut?"

In a flash the noisy little rivulets of trivial talk evaporated. There was a moment's pause as the weird possibilities of the idea began to take shape.

"Wow!" was the general, complimentary reaction.

"Gol-ly!" a few of them exclaimed. You could sense they were jockeying their verbal skiffs on the racing waters of their imaginations for the wild ride down the rapids.

"We could build a shack, and in a few years we'd have a skyscraper," the oldest kicked it off, a-thrill at the labor-saving possibilities.

"Yeah," said David, the engineer, "but it wouldn't have enough windows. Imagine a house ten stories high with only one row of windows."

"Or you could plant a toothpick in the ground," said another, "and after a while you'd have a telephone pole."

"Wood doesn't grow *that* fast," one of the girls objected. "It would take hundreds of years, wouldn't it, Daddy?"

"More or less," I agreed.

"What about people with wooden legs?"

"They'd grow to be giants."

"What makes wood grow anyway?" asked David. He was looking straight at me.

"Well," I coughed, "it's pretty complicated. Y'see—"

"Davie, dear," his mother came to my rescue again, "let's look it up in the encyclopedia after dinner, shall we?"

Half an hour later, the heads of the children were clustered like coconuts over the pages of the encyclopedia. "Daddy," said David, "did you know that sap runs up and down a tree like the blood in your veins?"

"Well, not exactly," I hedged, from behind the newspaper.

"Oh yes it does. It says so right here. The tree has veins just like you do."

Later that evening, after the children had gone to bed, Ginny surprised me peeking into the encyclopedia.

"I thought you were washing stockings or something," I said, easing the book back onto the shelf.

"Well," she said, "do trees have veins like you do?"

"Look," I said, guiltily, "how long have I been missing this sort of thing?"

"It's all right, dear," she smiled. "You've had a lot of things on your mind."

Next day I returned from work to find Nina and Danielle surrounded by a larger than usual group of neighbor children, who were obviously awaiting my arrival.

"Daddy," said Danielle, "*you* tell them. They won't believe you bought a fire engine."

9 · Bees Are Very Intelligent

"The little devils," Mr. Endicott mused, stroking his chin, and gazing with happy fascination at the front of our house. He said "little devils" the way you'd refer to bright, beautiful but mischievous children. He was referring, however, to bees.

Mr. Endicott raised bees—up to a point. I was going to follow the more accurate nomenclature of that interesting occupation and say he *kept* bees, but in this instance the statement would not be entirely true.

He had kept these bees until around three o'clock this afternoon, at which time they had risen in a body, left their hives beside his house, a quarter of a mile distant, and in a great, earth-darkening cloud had roared their way to our front yard.

I had been high on a ladder painting the second-floor window trim when the bees arrived. First there had been the noise, like the rumble of a deisel freight. For one wild moment I wondered if the St. Paul Railroad had detoured down our driveway. Then suddenly the sky was blackened by hundreds of tiny bodies, and there were the bees, not more than six feet from where I was painting. It was obvious they were going no farther.

I scrambled down the ladder, pursued by several dive bombers in their group. Once on the ground, I could see that while their interest centered on a spot high under the eaves, their swarming was so wild and erratic that all traffic through the front of the house would be effectively sealed off.

Mr. Endicott, in mesh headgear and gauntlets, had arrived shortly after the bees. He had followed their course across lawns, over fences, and through flower beds. A sparse, wiry man, in excellent physical condition, the chase had only exhilarated him.

"Why in the world don't they go home?" I asked.

He gave me the patient, tolerant look of the expert who realizes that in the face of such towering ignorance, any explanation of the subject would have to begin somewhere around the creation of the world.

"The habits of bees—" he began, sitting down on the grass.

A piercing scream from inside the house drowned out the buzzing of the bees and Mr. Endicott's quiet voice. A downstairs' window opened.

"Tim!" Ginny called, "Nina's been stung!"

"Ah-ha," said Mr. Endicott, rising. "Looks like they've found a way to get in." Then heads down, he and I plunged through the threatening mass.

Indoors, the front window of the living room was crawling with fluttering, angry little monsters.

"I was leaning on the radiator cover," Nina explained tearfully, "and all of a sudden a bee stung me."

"You probably put your hand down on top of one," said Mr. Endicott, as if Nina were at least seventy-five percent to blame.

"You mean," Ginny asked in panic, "they're *all* coming in here?"

Mr. Endicott wasn't listening. He was on his hands and knees peering at the window sill.

"The window wasn't open, if that's what you're thinking," Ginny defended herself against any further insinuations of carelessness from the bee expert.

"Ah-ha," Mr. Endicott said again. "They're getting in *here*." He pointed to an almost imperceptible chink between the base of the sill and the plaster of the wall, through which bees in close formation were parading confidently into the room.

"There's some putty in the basement," I called to Kip, who had joined the other children in watching the proceedings from the safety of the hallway. "Hurry!"

There was nothing for the rest of us to do but stand idly by and count the bees as they continued their forward march.

"Thirty-two, thirty-four, thirty-six," said Nina.

"You missed four over on the other end," said Danielle.

"The little devils," mused Mr. Endicott, fascinated.

At last Kip came back. "Couldn't find it," he said simply.

"Oh, Lord!"

"Well, I *couldn't*."

Then I raced to the basement myself. The putty had disappeared all right. I seized a roll of friction tape and rushed back upstairs.

"Cover it up with this," I gasped to Mr. Endicott, handing ing him the tape. I wasn't getting any closer to the bees than I had to.

As unconcerned as if stepping into a shower, Mr. Endicott moved in among the bees and began taping up the open space beneath the window sill.

"Bees are curious little creatures," he soothed us as he worked. "Very high intelligence. If you had the time to study them closely—"

Another scream told us David had been stung.

"I didn't even see him," he complained.

"They're apt to be excited at a time like this," Mr. Endicott said.

"Please," Ginny implored, "get them out of here!"

"You may find," Mr. Endicott continued in his calm, academic way, "that they'll discover other chinks to crawl through. You'll just have to keep an eye out for them."

"Then what?" I asked. "When the devil are they going home?"

"We have a problem there, I'm afraid," Mr. Endicott replied, straightening up. "You see, here's what's happened. The bees have followed the queen."

"And where's the queen?"

"Well," said Mr. Endicott, with his first show of concern, "I think she's settled somewhere in your wall."

"What?" Ginny gasped.

"And the whole swarm is going in there with her?" I asked.

"That's the way they are," sighed Mr. Endicott. "We must consider the problem of getting the queen."

Together we all considered it. It became increasingly clear, with every thoughtful second, that the problem had only one answer: tear out the wall.

"Once you get the queen," Mr. Endicott added, trying to lighten our burden, "you're all set."

"I wouldn't know her if I saw her," I said.

"She's much bigger than the rest," he explained.

"But won't she come out of her own free will?"

"Every hour she stays in there makes that solution less and less probable."

"But what will we *do?*" Ginny asked. She was already busy killing bees with a fly swatter, at every blow of which Mr. Endicott winced.

"Well," he said, sitting on the edge of the nearby desk, "I guess the best thing to do is just wait a while and see what happens. I don't think any more are getting into the room."

The whole thing, I began to fear, would ultimately shape up as a nice problem in apiary ethics. Should *we* be miffed because Mr. Endicott's bees were in *our* house? Or should *he* be put out because we seemed to be in possession of *his* bees? At any rate, I was annoyed by his calm attitude. The least he could do, I thought, was display more concern for *us*.

A figure moving across the lawn caught my eye. Mr. Tanning, a neighbor, was cautiously approaching the front door, his eyes wide with disbelief.

I rapped on the window and motioned him away.

"Be careful!" I shouted through the glass. "We have bees in here!"

Mr. Tanning considers himself quite a humorist.

"You'd better get busy," he called back. "You're losing a lot of them."

Bees were nothing to be afraid of, he assured us after he had carefully detoured around them and entered through the back door. "Have you ever been stung by a hornet?" he asked, in the superior way of a man who has seen everything.

Gradually the excitement diminished. Mrs. Tanning, who came over to remind her husband that it was time to start dressing for a dinner engagement that evening, stayed to hear Mr. Endicott elaborate on the social life of the bee.

"The workers," he declaimed with the easy authority of one who had studied the subject for years, "are sexually imperfect females, called neuters. If you observe them closely, you'll see they do not exhibit the same conformation as the males and queens."

"Well now!" said Mrs. Tanning.

I mixed highballs, and Ginny made up a tray of appetizers. Mrs. Endicott called to find her husband, and at Ginny's invitation, immediately joined us.

The Endicotts did most of the talking. The experience of the rest of us was limited to whether or not we had been stung recently. At one point Mrs. Tanning made an effort to change the subject, but without success. "I'm having the couch done over in blue after all," she whispered to Ginny.

"Bees," said Mr. Endicott firmly, "usually pass from flower to flower of the same kind, and not to flowers of different kinds indiscriminately. So you see what an important part they play in the economy of nature."

It was dusk when the party finally broke up. Mrs. Tanning had to phone her dinner hostess and say they had been unavoidably detained. The Endicotts promised to return next day with some good magazine articles and a book or two on bees. "As long as you have them," they said, "you might as well get to know them."

In the warm glow of good fellowship, we had temporarily forgotten about the front-door problem, and it was not until Mrs. Tanning, on the front step, yelped that she had been stung that we realized there was still work to be done.

"As I say, they're apt to be excited for a while," Mr. Endicott advised. "Try to keep them as calm as you can. If I were you, I'd use the back door exclusively for a few days."

Next morning, Ginny, however, had different plans. "We're not going to sit here quietly while the bees take over."

A few minutes earlier another neighbor, soliciting funds for the local park-improvement drive, had also been stung. The rest of us had been busy sealing up crevices which the bees had discovered under adjoining windows.

"It's a ticklish situation," I said. "I read a little about bees in the encyclopedia last night before I went to bed, and it seems that when a swarm of domestic bees can be identified by the owner of the original colony, he can claim them wherever they may alight."

"He may claim them, but can he collect them?" Ginny asked with a more practical view of the matter. "Nobody's going to tear our front wall down just to claim his old bees. I'm calling Mr. Tortelli right now!"

Mr. Tortelli was a jack of all trades. At Christmas time he sold Christmas trees. In spring he put in lawns. In winter he plowed snow. During the season of inch worms, he sprayed inch worms. He took down screens and put up storm windows, and took the storm windows down and put the screens back.

If a sewer clogged, if a roof leaked, if a baby wandered from home, you called Tortelli. If you had bees in your wall, Tortelli was your man.

Mr. Tortelli arrived at the wheel of a wheezing, flat-bed truck, on which he had mounted a gasoline engine, a huge compressor for spraying, and a network of racks that held extension ladders and coil after coil of two-inch hose.

His every movement inspired confidence. He was a tall, muscular Italian, swarthily handsome, with a masterpiece of a mustache, which he kept meticulously waxed, whatever the menial labor he was called to perform. Beneath the mustache was a perpetual smile of unassailable confidence, and teeth which, he boasted, had seen neither dentist nor cavity. "I never touch a drop," was Mr. Tortelli's explanation.

With him was his young assistant, an Italian relative, a thin, energetic young man, who apparently worshipped his employer. After each order from his boss, he would look at us, wink, and nod his head as if to say, "What do you think of *that* now. Isn't he wonderful?"

"Now then," said Mr. Tortelli, flashing his great smile, "where are those bees?" In the face of such gargantuan self-assurance, we felt embarrassed even to mention so small a thing as a bee.

Mr. Tortelli studied the situation under the eaves from several angles, like Michael Angelo considering where to position his figure of God. "We put the ladder over there and blow them west—no good. They get stuck in trees and come back."

"Are you going to *blow* them away?" I asked incredulously.

"Blow them away and kill them good," laughed Mr. Tortelli. "What I shoot on these bees she kill a horse." He walked to the other side of the lawn and considered the situation from a fresh viewpoint.

"I think," he said at last, pulling meditatively at his nose, "we blow them east."

His assistant winked, nodded, and ran to fetch the ladders.

Tortelli mounted the truck, where he opened several bags of powdered material, which he poured into the tank of the compressor. "This stuff, she kill a horse," he assured us again.

Then turning over the engine to the younger man, he

mounted the ladders with the agility of a cat, the hoses coiled around his neck and shoulders. His assistant crouched over the pounding engine of the truck tense and ready.

"We blow these damn bees clear to Benton Harbor," Mr. Tortelli sang from the top rung. He hooked an arm around the ladder to brace himself, and aimed the nozzle at the center of the swarm of bees. "Start the engine!"

With the force and fury of a hundred hurricanes a spray as thick as all the fogs of London burst from the end of Mr. Tortelli's hose. The branches bent with the gale, the shutters rattled on nearby windows. A musty vortex of swirling leaves and winter-old silt rose from the gutters, hung for a moment in the air, then spun furiously out of sight over the neighboring rooftops and trees.

It was over as swiftly as it began. There was not a sign of a bee to mar the pristine purity of the freshly washed landscape. From the top of the ladder Mr. Tortelli bowed.

When the bees came back next morning (presumably on the boat from Benton Harbor), I called Mr. Endicott.

"You still haven't found the queen," he reminded me gently.

"But why did the others come back? Doesn't DDT and all that other stuff have any effect on bees?"

"I wouldn't know," he said, a note of reproach in his voice. "I never tried to *kill* a bee."

"Dad," said Kip at breakfast a few mornings later, his face bright with a new idea, "why don't *we* keep bees like Mr. Endicott?"

"What do you think we're doing now?"

"I mean *really* keep them—in hives."

"I think that would be a *wonderful* idea," said Ginny. "That would be a very instructive hobby for the boys."

"I've had enough of bees to do me for the rest of my life," I said with feeling.

"But Mr. Endicott told me he'd help me build the hive."

"Isn't that wonderful, Tim?" asked Ginny.

"Let's think it over and talk about it later."

The boys, abetted by their mother, had been spending more and more time with Mr. Endicott. "Do you realize," David said one evening before falling asleep, "bees have three eyes on the top of their heads?"

"That's fine," I said. "Now go to sleep."

"That's so they can see what's going on better when their heads are stuck in flowers."

"Good night, David."

"If we had bees, we'd have a lot of honey free."

Our living room had become a kind of natural-history museum, with groups of neighborhood children trooping through the house at Kip's and Dave's invitation to stand with their ears against the front wall and hear the buzzing inside.

"It's fun to be so near them and not get stung," one giggling seven year old reported.

"Our teacher said this was a wonderful opportunity to study the ways of nature," a bespeckled scholar informed me. "I'd like to bring some more of the class over tomorrow."

"Absolutely," said David.

The bees continued to make the front yard uninhabitable to everyone but the children, who moved among them with the assurance of Mr. Endicott.

"They've calmed down now," Kip explained. "They won't bother you if you don't bother them. Mr. Endicott told me."

Mr. Endicott had become the authority on everything except how to get rid of bees.

"You're suppose to eat your peas with a fork," Nina informed us at dinner. "Mr. Endicott said so."

"You've never heard *us* tell you that?" I asked her.

"Nope," said Nina.

I had tried every strategy to make the bees feel unwelcome. "If I could only get close enough to see where they're getting in," I told one neighbor, "I'd seal up the opening."

"Smoke is the only answer," he replied. "Soak a rag in kerosene and tie it to the end of a broom handle and hold it up there under the eaves."

All the smoke did was smudge the front of the house.

"You're only getting them excited," Kip, the naturalist, said, with annoyance.

I sprayed the area again and again with the strongest solution of DDT I could buy. Like Mr. Tortelli, the druggist I bought it from assured me it was strong enough to kill a horse. I began to wish we *did* have horses in the walls. It would have been a cinch to get rid of them.

The least I can do, I told myself one day, is finish painting the front trim. If the bees don't bother the kids, I don't see why they should bother me.

With a manly show of confidence I mounted the ladder and began painting. I had taken no more than one of two strokes when the bees came at me buzzing angrily. I swiped at them in self-defense with the only weapon I had, the wet paint brush. A series of zig-zag splotches of fresh green paint across the white clapboard house front marked the frenzy of my descent down the ladder.

Mr. Endicott explained. "They probably don't like the smell of paint."

"And you got them excited again," Kip added.

The children, and even Ginny now, were accepting the bees as members of the family. "I walked right through them today, and they didn't bother me once," Ginny said one evening.

"Sure," said Kip. "Leave *them* alone and they'll leave *you* alone."

Then a few days later, arriving home after dark, I noticed a strange thing. There were no bees!

They've gone, I congratulated myself. The blasted little nuisances have gone at last.

I told Ginny. "Gone?" she said, puzzled. "Are you sure?" We pressed our ears to the soiled spot on the wall where innumerable neighborhood heads and hands had left a dark, oily stain. Inside was the familiar buzzing, less noisy perhaps, but still there.

"They're going to sleep for the night," Ginny explained, with what sounded like relief.

Asleep for the night, I muttered to myself as I crawled into bed. The kids, Ginny, the bees and me—asleep for the night.

Then I sat up, wide awake. If the bees were all in bed—

"What's the matter, dear?" Ginny asked.

"Nothing," I whispered, trying to be calm. "I'm going downstairs to—to check the back door. Just go to sleep."

I put on my bedroom slippers and tiptoed down the stairs to the basement workshop and rummaged around on the shelves. Yes, thank Heaven, there it was, a package of fast-drying patching plaster. I found an old tin can and mixed a batch with water from the laundry tap. Then I picked up a flashlight and went out to the garage. Loaded down with plaster, flashlight, and extension ladder, I crept quietly to the front of the house.

If no one sees me, I thought, I'll be all right.

I trained the flashlight on the eaves above the door. Not a bee in sight. With complete confidence I mounted the ladder. At that moment a lone bee, returning from who knows what pollinated revels, reeled uncertainly up to the wall, crawled around for a moment, like a guilty husband sneaking home after hours, and then disappeared inside. "Thanks!" I said fervently. He had betrayed the opening.

My putty knife flashed in the moonlight. The plaster went on as smooth as cream. When I had finished I carefully scraped the area clean so that from a few feet away no one could tell that anything had been tampered with.

Ginny was sound asleep when I returned to bed.

There was bedlam the next morning.

"The bees are gone!" the children cried aghast.

"The bees are gone!" Ginny echoed.

"Gone?" I asked "Are you sure?"

We listened at the wall. The buzzing was loud and growing louder. "That's funny," Ginny said. "There isn't a sign of a bee *outside*."

"Maybe," I said smugly, "they overslept."

She looked at me sharply. "Exactly where did *you* go last night?"

"Down to check the back door. It was open all right," I added.

"You didn't go outside?"

"Oh, I know what you're thinking," I said boldly. "But would I go outside in my pajamas? And up a ladder? In the pitch dark?"

It *did* sound preposterous when you left out the flashlight.

"Well," she said, listening at the wall again, *"something's* wrong."

"Do you suppose?" I asked innocently, "a little piece of plaster could have got in the way?"

"You *could* have used a flashlight," she said.

"Wouldn't *that* have attracted a lot of attention!"

"All I know is the children are broken hearted."

Kip called up Mr. Endicott. He arrived exclaiming that never in all his experience had anything so strange happened.

"Ordinarily," he said, "when they stay inside like that, it means they're getting ready to swarm some place else with a second queen. But these bees just got here, so to speak. I don't see how they'd be ready to swarm so soon."

He stared fixedly at the eaves, hoping for one tiny bee to show its head. But I had done my work well. Not a bee, not a sign of plaster.

"There seem to be ladder marks here," Ginny said, prodding the ground inquisitively with her toe.

"There ought to be," I replied bravely. "Think of the time I tried to finish the painting." I was master of the situation, with an answer for any question.

"Well," said Mr. Endicott, "I'm blamed if I know what to do." I knew what he was *thinking* of doing—tearing a hole in the wall.

"Well," I said easily, pressing a droplet of white plaster into the ground with my shoe. "I guess we've just got to wait."

"You're right," he admitted. "The little devils."

"Hi, there!" It was Mr. Tanning driving up to offer me a ride to the station.

"The bees are gone," I told him happily.

"So *that* explains it," he said.

"What explains *what?*" Ginny asked.

"Mae and the kids were driving home from the movies last night—" Mr. Tanning began.

"—and they saw a strange creature crawling up a ladder with a flashlight," Ginny finished.

"They could only see the light," Mr. Tanning corrected her, with a fine feeling for the truth. "What's the matter?" he asked, seeing the downward set of Ginny's eyebrows, "Didn't you *want* to get rid of the bees?"

Later that week, Mr. Endicott brought over a great quantity of fresh honey to show there were no hard feelings.

"A little present for the children," he explained. "They seem to be pretty heartbroken about their bees." He went to the wall and listened. The buzzing had all but stopped. "The poor little devils," he sighed, throwing me a brief, censuring look. I had adamantly refused to remove my plaster patch.

"How is it," I asked, "that *you* have honey? I thought the bees were all over here."

"Oh," he replied, "that was just *one* swarm that followed a new queen. I still have another queen and another swarm— why, what's the matter?"

10 · No Home Should Be Without One

I will never completely understand my family's attitude toward animals. There were times when it looked as if Ginny had mothered a large brood just to have extra excuses for adopting dogs, cats, and other (so-called) household pets.

"Every child should have a dog," we had agreed in the early months of her first pregnancy. Dogs help build a child's character. Dogs develop a child's sense of responsibility. Dogs provide a child with the affection he needs—in case his parents back down, I suppose.

Dogless children lead lonely, twisted lives that in many cases end in the criminal court. No child of ours was going to lead a lonely, twisted life that might end in the criminal court.

We congratulated ourselves that we were facing the problem in plenty of time. Our child wasn't going to have one single tiny fraction of a life's moment without one of man's best friends around to help develop his sense of responsibility. One of the first faces to greet him on arrival in this world would be the hairy muzzle of some loyal pup.

Our plans, however, were soon blown sky high. The owner of the apartment building in which we were living said flatly, "No dogs."

Not until six years later, when we moved to a home in a Chicago suburb, were we able to give Kip the canine friendship we were sure he so sorely needed, but which, now that I look back on it, he had done very well without. The day after moving in, we acquired a German-shepherd puppy, already named Tambo.

He was the most intelligent dog I ever owned and certainly the most economical. We never had to feed him, because he pilfered food from the neighbors. He took it from their garbage cans, upsetting the contents all over their lawns, or stole it from their back porches at delivery time. He knew the schedule of every grocer and milkman in the neighborhood. Many a housewife's complaint to her dairy that she never received her cottage cheese or butter could be traced to Tambo's facility for being on her back porch at exactly the critical instant between the milkman's departure and her own arrival.

Tambo's genius for discovering who on the grocer's delivery route was not at home that day soon put a stop to that man's easy-going custom of leaving groceries on back doorsteps, and

made housewives think twice before going out for the afternoon.

When asked why we didn't feed the dog ourselves, I could
only answer truthfully, "He never seems to be hungry."

As he grew older, however, Tambo developed an unaccount-
able animosity toward an inoffensive seven-year-old girl
across the street. At the sound of her voice or footstep, he
would streak, howling like a timber wolf, in her direction.
The little girl, shrieking hysterically for her mother, would
race for the safety of her front doorway. Thank God, she
always made it.

My apologies and protestations that Tambo wouldn't hurt
a fly were not only inadequate, they were not based on fact.
One of his liveliest diversions was snapping at flies.

At last, even the tears of Ginny and the children were
unable to stay the wrath of the neighborhood, and Tambo
went to live in a friend's childless home, where, by last reports, his personality has undergone a complete change. With
no boys to save from lonely, twisted lives, he has settled down
to being a respectable household pet, who takes all his meals
on his own doorstep.

A buff-colored cocker spaniel, named Jeff, replaced Tambo,
but since David was on the scene by then, we naturally had
to have a second dog, too. One boy at a time is enough for
any dog, we figured, so we found ourselves another buff-
colored cocker named, with little imagination, Buff. The fact
that Buff was Jeff's daughter meant nothing to Jeff. He hated
her with a deep and howling hate. The two dogs had to be
kept at opposite ends of the house and aired separately. For
years, until Jeff finally outgrew his unpaternal feelings, progress from one end of the house to the other was at the speed of

a canal boat going through the locks. You didn't enter or leave a room until you were sure all doors behind you were securely closed.

First of the children to display any unusual talents for handling animals was David, who gave evidence of this trait in a way that had us shivering for months whenever we thought of it.

One sunny afternoon, when he was three, news flashed around the neighborhood that a cat "as big and wild as a wildcat" was on the loose, scaring the wits out of grownups and children alike. Several youngsters displayed deep scratches to prove the beast's viciousness.

Of course, with every hour, the cat became bigger and more savage, until finally a frantic neighbor, who discovered it hiding under her backsteps, vowed that it *was* a wildcat, and ran inside to call the police.

When the police arrived, however, the cat was gone, and an hour's careful search through flower beds and under porches failed to show any trace of it.

That evening, as we sat down to dinner, David calmly announced that a big yellow cat and four kittens were in our garage.

"Whereabouts in the garage?" I gasped. I had put the car away only a few minutes before and had seen no cats.

"Behind the storm windows in the corner where she always is," said David. "Want me to show you?"

"You stay here," his mother commanded shakily.

A fast peek behind the storm windows showed me that David had been telling the truth. There *was* a yellow cat, the biggest yellow cat I had ever seen, and she was nursing four of the biggest nursing kittens I had ever seen.

"Call the police," Ginny insisted. "I'd die if you stayed in there another minute."

The police, a little out of sorts by now at the great cat myth, walked brazenly into the garage and turned back the storm windows. A moment later they were scurrying back to their squad car in search of gloves and some kind of blunt weapon. The danger of ricocheting bullets ruled out the use of guns.

Armed with long sticks and a gunny sack, the men reentered the garage and closed the door behind them. Ginny, the boys and myself watched through a window.

Their idea, evidently, was to pin the cat down with the sticks, then snare it in the gunny sack. To that plan, however, the cat had effective counter measures. She kept to the high places where it was almost impossible to touch her, even with a stick, and at unexpected moments swooped down in brief, darting forays that invariably caught the police off guard. Her shrieks and hissings filled the air like the sound of a caliope played by a madman. From behind the storm windows the four nursing kittens howled their protests.

"I can't stand this," Ginny said. "I'm going back to the house."

I looked at the two boys. Their noses were pressed flat against the window pane. I couldn't have pried them loose if I tried.

At last the cat grew too bold. She leaped at one of the men who happened to be in a good position for counterattack, and in another instant she caught the force of his stick on her underbelly and the wind was knocked out of her. One of the others wrapped her quickly in the sack and the struggle was over. The four kittens were an easy catch once the mother was subdued.

A few drinks later, the police departed. David was standing alone at a front window watching the squad car back down the driveway. There were tears in his eyes.

"Why couldn't we keep the kittens anyway?" he sniffled.

"Why, dear," Ginny said, "they'd grow up to be wild just like their mother."

"But she isn't *wild*," David protested. "She was nice. She liked it when I patted her."

"You *patted* her?" Ginny managed to gasp.

"Lots of times," said David. "Days and days."

"Dear," said his mother, "why didn't you tell us sooner?"

"I was afraid somebody would take her away."

Only our solemn promise to get him a kitten of his own finally consoled him. But even then he had conditions. "Four," he said stubbornly, "just like the others."

One evening, when David was five, he failed to turn up in time for dinner, and I went out to fetch him. A search of his usual haunts brought no results, and I was walking down a street farther from home than he had ever before ventured when I met one of his playmates homeward bound, a look of near panic on his face.

"What's the matter?" I asked.

"David," he gulped.

"Where is he?"

"In the tree."

"Where, where?"

"Next block."

"Show me!" I yelled, and started running. As we hurried along, David's friend filled in a few more details.

"It's Mr. Grumley's tree . . . he doesn't like the owls . . . they make too much noise . . . he put the ladder against the tree and then went back in the house for some-thing."

"Save your breath." I had heard enough.

The ladder was a long, extension type, and it leaned fully extended against the uppermost branches of a dead tree. At the very top stood David. A hole about a foot in diameter was in the trunk, and David's arm, up to the shoulder, was in the hole.

I mustn't startle him, I breathed to myself; he might fall.

"David," I called, as calmly as I could, "you'd better come down."

He swung around on the ladder like a sailor born to the crow's nest, and waved at me.

"Be careful!" I shouted.

"Don't worry, Daddy!" he called back. "I'm not hurting them. I'm only patting their feathers!"

That was the attitude that prevailed in all our relationships with the animal kingdom, never fear, only concern for the beasts themselves. Like when I shooed away a footloose horse which seemed intent on entering our kitchen. ("You should have gone with him, Daddy; now he'll get lost.")

When Peggy, our fifth, was born, we had to admit we had outgrown our house in the suburbs, and so we moved to our present house "in the country."

The "country" meant only one thing to the children—un-limited opportunities for raising animals. During our first weeks in the new place, scarcely a day went by without news that someone's cat or dog or rabbit had just borne a family, and as soon as the young ones were weaned, we were offered first choice.

Our choice, in most cases, consisted of as many of the litter as the children could carry. At one time there were five dogs, six cats, six ducks, a rabbit, a parakeet, a dove, and two horses on the premises.

Generally, cats in such quantities became less desirable as they grew up. They raised havoc with the bird population. On the other hand, they kept the place singularly clear of mice. Mostly, we compromised by keeping one or two; the rest we would give away to local farmers who always seemed glad to have cats around their barns. The giving-away period usually lasted from a week to two months, because the cats would return night after night, no matter how firmly we deposited them with the farmers next morning.

The six ducks were done in one night by a fox, and for long afterward my great fear was that somehow the fox would be found, tamed, and added to our list of pets.

The dove was not given to us, but arrived by his own choice. He landed outside our back door one morning, almost at David's feet, and forthwith abandoned all interest in flying. For several weeks he followed David around on foot like a dog. In fact the dogs must have thought he *was* a dog, for they treated him with effortless camaraderie.

One morning, however, Dave found the dove floundering in our tiny garden pool, all but dead. He placed it on its back, knelt over it, and for several minutes, administered artificial respiration. For every drop of water he squeezed out of the dove, his tears added a dozen more.

When the dove finally died, a second parakeet was purchased to take its place.

One thing the children were learning was that wherever there is so much life, the chances of death grow in proportion. Their bitterest experience, and one that gave me a wholly new insight into the depths of a boy's affections, concerned one of the horses.

But we must start at the beginning. The acquiring of our horses followed much the same roundabout pattern by which we got most of our pets.

The farmer next door boarded horses, among which was a strong and frisky stallion. The horse's owner had warned me not to let the boys near him under any circumstances, as the animal was entirely unpredictable.

"Don't worry," I assured him. "The boys have no interest in horses. They don't even know the first thing about riding."

He gave me a queer look, which I was not to understand until several days later.

It was Saturday morning. Ginny and I were returning earlier than expected from shopping. As we came up our driveway, which borders one of the farmer's fields, we were dumbfounded to discover Kip galloping around in circles on a mare, with David close behind atop the stallion. Both were riding bareback and having the time of their lives.

When David caught sight of us, he waved his hand in a vain attempt at bravado, and then sheepishly but (I noted with pride) expertly headed the stallion back to the barn.

From that day on their interest in horses increased, or at least became more public. I saw the signs of the inevitable, but fought against it as bravely as I could. Raised in the city, where I learned to ride a bicycle on a busy street-car line, I nevertheless felt that horseback riding, even in the country, was too dangerous for youngsters. Besides, it was too expensive. Neither argument had much effect on the boys or their mother.

One day Kip announced that one of the mares was about to foal, and the mare's owner promised Kip he would give us first chance to buy the colt. The price was reasonable for anyone with a few hundred dollars he didn't know what to do with. The fact that I didn't fit this description had little bearing on the subsequent purchase.

This, however, created a second problem. Whose horse was it—Kip's or Dave's?

An uncle of mine resolved the whole question by buying us a second horse, a mare of dubious age, who became David's charge by virtue of the fact that he was the only one of us she didn't try to bite.

Eventually, by sheer kindness, he broke her of her biting habit, and she became a loved and respected member of the family. I must admit it was a source of great pride to watch the boys' mastery of the animals increase day by day, and to witness their spirited exhibitions of horsemanship, as I was called to do whenever it was time to buy another supply of hay or oats.

Then one winter's morning, when Dave and Kip went out to the garage-turned-stable to feed the animals, they found David's horse lying on the floor, unable to do more than lift her head. Frantically, the veterinarian was summoned, and he diagnosed the trouble as a spinal infection that is nearly always fatal.

David refused to believe that death would take such a big beautiful creature as his horse. For two days he stayed with the animal constantly, sitting up as late as eleven o'clock each night, with the dying horse's head in his lap. Brought to bed forcibly, he set the alarm for 4 A.M., and in the dark, freezing morning, bundled to the ears, he trudged back to the garage alone and sat again on the floor, stroking the big head, brushing its neck, and trying to force a few drops of water down the throat.

On the third morning he knew it was no use. At seven o'clock he came back to the house and, trembling, told his mother, "She's having some kind of a fit. I can't stop her. She doesn't know me any more."

He returned to the garage and stayed with his horse until the big truck came and the man swung down with the rifle.

Then David ran sobbing to the house, where his mother held him in her arms, in a clothes closet, so neither of them would hear the shot.

"We'll pray for another horse," Ginny consoled him in the days that followed.

As David visualized it, the new horse would be young, a yearling, if possible, one that he could break to the saddle himself. It would also have a touch of Arabian blood, to give it the delicate head of that beautiful breed. On the third point he was not insistent, but he hoped it would be pinto colored.

To bring this fabulous creature closer to reality, he dispatched queries to horse breeders he had looked up in several horse magazines. Then a few days later he came to me, half-hoping, half-despairing, the breeder's answers in his hand, and said, "Eight-hundred dollars is pretty much money, isn't it, Daddy?"

One Sunday afternoon the miracle happened. I was reading the newspaper in the living room when David ran to answer the phone, as he usually does. A few minutes of excited conversation, then he called to me: "It's a girl in town. She heard I wanted a horse!"

"Ask her how much and what kind it is," I suggested.

Another few seconds of buzzing questions and answers, then David called again: "She wants to *give* it to me. They don't have enough room for it. They just want it to have a nice home."

More questions and answers over the wire, then the un-believable climax of the great news: "Daddy! It's a yearling! It's half quarter-horse and half Arabian—*and it's a pinto!*"

As I say, I will never completely understand my family's attitude toward animals. One midnight not long ago I was awakened by noises in the hallway outside our bedrooms. A moment later the hall light went on, to reveal Kip standing with clenched fists outside the door that leads to the attic.

"There's someone coming down the attic stairs," he gulped.

I listened. There was a muffled flop-flop as if someone in loose bedroom slippers were descending the steps.

"Open the door and jump back," I said, preparing to meet the lady head-on.

Kip pulled the door open. From the bottom step a dark, flapping shadow rose and circled erratically about our heads. It was a bat.

Offhand I can't tell you the measurements of the average bat, but however modest they may be, this one, at midnight, looked like an eagle. Fearsome memories of Dracula and the Bat Man crowded my mind as the bat steered himself, by slow and deliberate flappings, into the room where Nina and Danielle were asleep. There he flew in great circles, barely missing the heads of the girls each time around.

I reached to turn on the lamp beside Nina's bed, hoping she would not awake before I had rid the room of this monster. The lamp, however, had been disconnected. The socket was behind the headboard. I pushed the bed away from the wall just as Nina opened her eyes.

"What's the matter, Daddy?" she asked.

"Nothing," I panted. "I'm just fixing your light. Go back to sleep!" She took me at my word and closed her eyes.

Meanwhile, the bat had been circling the room steadily, fanning the top of my head with his wings each time he passed. You mustn't let a bat get into your hair, I thought, remembering some choice horror stories about these flying mice, or he'll nest there. And you won't be able to get him out until you shave your head. I don't remember which thought terrified me most, a bat in my hair, or my head clean shaven. Also, if it's the vampire type, it'll drink your blood. See Byrnes if you want to know about bats!

Across the room on a chair lay the girls' clothing. In the dim light of the bedside lamp, I clutched a blouse or skirt or something of the sort, waited for the bat to come around once more, then leaped in the air, swung the garment and smothered him to the floor. Holding him firmly, I carried him, squealing and fluttering, to the nearest window and hurled him into the night. I felt I had rid the house of something no less awful than the bubonic plague.

Next morning, as modestly as the truth would permit, I told Ginny what had happened.

"Oh," she said, her face clouding over, "you shouldn't have done that."

"What?"

"Bats are very friendly," she said. "I was reading an article only last week that said it's *very* easy to train them."

"Yeah," said Kip, coming to the doorway, "and it was such a *cute* little bat."

11 · Who's Afraid of the Future?

There was a time when I could read the insurance ads ("How Secure is THEIR Future?") without a second glance. Even when our family included two or three children, I saw little connection between them and the two or three orphans-to-be in the ads, waiting at their mother's knee for the father who would never return. Me, I would always return.

Eventually, however, the years, the sheer number of my children, or cars that came too close for comfort made me more and more aware of my responsibilities. I began to pay attention to the families in the illustrations, even though they showed no inclination to keep up with me in the number of offspring. In this respect, at any rate, their future was proving to be a lot more secure than mine.

At last it was impossible for me to read the ad man's challenging question without seeing Ginny's features in the face of the mother, and several of my children sprinkled in among the others. Maybe some fine night I *wouldn't* return!

A careful review of my insurance program told me that in such an emergency my family would have a choice of two courses. They could collect all my insurance immediately and live like kings for about two months, but after that, babies and all, they would be on their own. Or they could take advantage of the monthly sustenance plan, and out of periodic payments keep themselves almost indefinitely in, say, handkerchiefs.

The first plan was frowned upon by the insurance company as being improvident. "Unless your wife is used to handling large amounts of money," I was told, "a lump sum might soon be dissipated. And *then* where would they be?" The second procedure was far more sensible and businesslike. "At least they'll always have *something* coming in."

To my frantic appeal for an insurance plan that would give my ten dependents adequate protection over a long period of years, my insurance broker outlined a program, the basic requirement of which was that I should immediately get a job paying five times more than I was earning. With each attempt to bring the program closer to what I could afford, the closer it approached the "little-something-each-month" plan already in force.

"Even if I make a million," I told Ginny, with a fine disregard for the laws of probability, "the best I can leave you is a few month's security at most."

"When do you plan on going?" she asked.

"It's not funny," I said. "A father has to think of these things, especially a father with this many kids."

"All right, so you've thought of them. Do you feel better?"

"I wish I had brains enough to develop a little business of my own, instead of wasting all this time trying to be a writer. A business means security."

"I wish you had brains enough to work harder at being a writer instead of wasting all this time worrying," Ginny replied. She had a persistent notion that anything I wrote would keep the family in furs for life.

"But a guy with a business has something tangible to leave his family, something that will keep working for them after he's gone. What's a writer going to leave his family? His old typewriter!"

Ginny sniffled. "It might be wonderful to leave your children your old typewriter. They might want it more than anything else in the world."

The discussion ended on this misty-eyed note.

The idea of a business of my own, however, persisted. "Byrnes and Sons"—I could see the nameplate clearly, words that would signify economic independence for generations of Byrneses yet unborn. The only problem was what kind of business?

Byrnes and Sons—Movers? The boys were a little young to be of much use in a broad-shouldered enterprise like that. Byrnes and Sons—Exterminators? No experience. Groceries? What did *we* know about the grocery business? Excavating? Furniture? Sand and Gravel? Tree Surgeons?

Don't force it, I told myself. Someday, unexpectedly, the answer will come. But in the meantime, stay away from those insurance ads.

Then one day, unexpectedly, the answer did come.

It came while I was doodling some pencil sketches for the

amusement of the younger children. I had drawn a puppy
dog's face, wearing a big frown. "Make him happy," one of
the youngsters demanded. I drew him with a smile.

"*Well*," I said to myself. My sketching became more pur-
poseful.

"What wide shoulders the dog has," one of the children
said.

"He doesn't have any feet," another complained.

"He isn't supposed to," I muttered. "Now keep quiet."

The children were baffled by my sudden change of attitude.

"What is it?" one of them finally ventured.

"A coat hanger, of course," I said triumphantly. "A coat
hanger for kids. A puppy dog's head—see? And here are the
shoulders where you hang the clothes. No clothes, he frowns.
Hang up a coat and what happens? Big smile."

The children danced. "Make one now, Daddy!"

During the next few days I made several, experimenting
with different expressions and mechanisms. I finally developed one to the point where the weight of a fairly light garment sufficed to draw down a portion of the dog's face and
change the expression from a frown to a smile. Remove the
garment, and a hidden rubber band, later a spring, drew the
face together again in the frown.

How secure was *their* future? They were safe forever.

Ginny admitted it was a cute idea, but wouldn't it take me
away from the book I was planning? Let the book wait, I
told her. Security comes before everything else. Security for
all those kids. Byrnes and Sons—Coat Hangers.

It was to be a mail-order business, at least to begin with,
operated from our basement, which would also be the factory.
Mail order appealed to me for several reasons. I would have
direct contact with the consumer. I would be my own adver-

tising agency. I could more or less control the demand until the supply was up to it. And there would be no middle man to water down the profits.

"For a person who can't keep his own checking account in balance, a business of his own is a pretty risky thing, don't you think?" Ginny suggested.

"Don't worry," I said. "I'll learn. And in time the boys will help me. Remember—Byrnes and Sons."

"But how will you ever find time to *make* all those hangers yourself? It takes you so long to make just one."

"That's because we don't have it down to an assembly-line system yet," I explained. "With a few power tools, like a band saw and a drill press, we'll turn those things out like peanuts."

After some debate it was agreed the business ought to bear a more attractive name than Byrnes and Sons. Children's coat hangers seemed to call for something more pixie-like. Eventually, at Ginny's suggestion, it was named Hickory Knoll Workshop after the original Hickory Knoll Farm, of which our house had once been a part.

Columbus provisioning for his first voyage could have experienced no stronger sense of destiny than I did in lining up my production materials. There were many things to buy: lumber, that would have to be silk-screened with the likeness of the pup; a power band saw for cutting the dog's outline from the wood; a sanding machine, a drill press, cardboard cartons for mailing the finished product; labels and stationery, string, glue, stamps, a logo, or signature, for the ads I would place.

Steadily the tide of boxes, wood and other materials overflowed the basement storage spaces and rose in a flood up stairwells, into closets, and at last to the attic. "We have to

be ready to fill those orders the minute they come in," I told
a protesting Ginny.

All this preparation was done in what I referred to then as
my spare time. My employer at the time, more and more
aware of my late arrivals and early departures, had another
name for it. Each day he became less patient with my telephoned excuse that "Things are kind of mixed up at home,
and I'll be a few minutes late."

"They're mixed up all right," Ginny would mumble, trying
to extricate a vacuum cleaner or floor mop from the tangle of
boxes and wrapping paper on the basement stairs.

I rewrote the ad copy dozens of times. "Untidiness be
hanged with Hanger Pup!" the final headline exclaimed.
Mothers were promised that this great new invention ($1.50
each, 3 for $4.00) would make it such fun to hang up clothes
that youngsters would soon fall into undreamed-of habits of
neatness.

At last, convinced that I was ready for business, I took
what funds I had left and bought a small ad in one of the
popuar "home" magazines. A good time to advertise, I told
myself, just six weeks before Christmas. Then I waited, serenely confident, mentally snapping my fingers at the future.
Neighbors and friends waited, too, a little skeptical. Ginny
waited, a little sad.

Three or four days after the ad appeared, the mail brought
a request for one hanger. One hanger! Where was the great
spontaneous national response I expected? I began to think
dark thoughts about the magazine's claims of readership.

"Why don't you make a few hangers now," Ginny suggested, "so that when the orders come in, you won't keep the
people waiting?"

"Plenty of time for that," I replied. "I want some indication first of how many I'll need. The smart manufacturer has to learn to pace himself."

The next few days brought several orders, some for sets of three. The week end brought a dozen more. Sunday morning I added up the requests and found to my amazement that there were no less than fifty hangers to be made.

I descended to the basement. The hour had come. Production must start at once!

In spite of the "assembly-line" technique, the work of cutting, matching, sanding, polishing, packaging, and addressing the hangers took longer than I thought. By midnight Sunday I had finished only thirty.

The Monday morning mail brought orders for twenty-five more. I called up the office and told them I wasn't feeling well and wouldn't be in today. Then I went back to the basement. As I worked, I fought down a faint, but unmistakable, feeling of panic.

"I thought the boys were going to help," Ginny said. "Remember—Byrnes and Sons?"

"They have helped," I said, "if you want to call it help." For the first ten minutes the boys had been enthusiastic and energetic. I had given Dave the job of rough cutting the hanger sections from the silk-screened plywood, and Kip the task of sanding certain pieces smooth.

Then Dave cut his finger and had to give up for the day. I thought Kip was doing his work with remarkable concentration until his over-the-shoulder question, "Do you think this hole is too big for a wren?" led me to investigate. He had long since finished the sanding and was making a birdhouse.

Miffed by my violent reaction, he returned to the original job. "But it gets so monotonous," he complained.

Dave, nursing his cut finger, squatted outside the basement window, talking to Kip about the game of touchball they were supposed to take part in that afternoon. "Do you think we can go, Dad?" Kip asked.

"You're in business," I told him. "Do you think touchball is more important than business?" He refused to answer. At three o'clock there was nothing to do but let them go and play touchball. They returned that evening, too tired to help with the work.

"Look," I said finally, "this is a joint venture. A kind of family enterprise. It won't work unless *everybody* helps." They admitted they had been lax, but promised to be more cooperative in the future. To their credit it must be said that once they buckled down to the work, they stuck to it.

But even with the boys' help, and an occasional hand from Ginny, it was impossible to keep up with the orders. I had simply miscalculated the time it would take to turn out a hanger, assembly-line technique or no assembly-line technique. Nor was it much help to take off more and more days from my regular job, on the plea that "I haven't been up to snuff lately."

By the third and fourth weeks I was receiving, in addition to a deluge of orders, letters from customers complaining that the merchandise had not arrived. Follow-up letters, sharper in tone, and mixed in with "Get-Well-Quick" cards from the office, contained only a flat "Where is it?"

"The sensible thing to do," Ginny suggested one morning around 2 A.M. as I tumbled into bed, "is to get someone else to make the hangers for you—a small factory, for instance. Then you sell them. That's what *smart* inventors do. They don't waste their time on a lot of messy details."

That was the ticket, all right. Keep my mind free to dream up other inventions. Of course! Why hadn't I thought of that myself?

"I'll stop in tomorrow at that woodworking place near the station," I promised.

"And then," Ginny replied, as she rolled over to go to sleep, "get on the train and give your employer some of your time."

Mr. Ivar Swanson, of the Excelsior Woodturning Company, emerged from the shop behind his office, brushing sawdust from his arms and overalls in a thick yellow cloud.

"Vell," he boomed in a hearty Swedish accent, "ay hope you're not in a hurry. Ve nefer so busy all year."

I held out the coat hanger. Mr. Swanson's broad, honest face showed only puzzlement. "Yah?" he said. "So?"

I waited for the slow smile of recognition, the unbelieving shake of the head in admiration for such ingeniousness. "So?" Mr. Swanson persisted.

"It's a coat hanger," I said. "Look—see how it works?"

Mr. Swanson stared fixedly at the frowning, smiling face of the pup.

"A coat hanger?" he asked uncertainly.

"For children," I said. "It encourages them to hang up their clothes."

Mr. Swanson laughed. "My youngest boy, he thirty-seven last veek. Ve don't need no coat hanger."

I assured him I wasn't trying to sell him the coat hanger, but was looking for someone to manufacture them for me in quantity—and at the lowest possible price.

He worked the hanger several times, staring at the puppy

features as if half expecting them to bark. I removed the back piece so he could see the mechanism inside.

"It's nice," he said finally. "But ay couldn't do it."

"You couldn't?"

"Too many pieces. Too hard to put together."

"But *I* can put it together," I protested.

Mr. Swanson smiled tolerantly. "Yah, but ve are in business to make money. Ve make this coat hanger, you know how much it cost? Three-four dollars. You mark up another two-three dollars. Who buys a coat hanger for six-seven dollars?"

"But *I* make it to sell for $1.50," I said.

Mr. Swanson laughed. "You're a genius."

Other woodworking shops I visited made it plain that to get the price down to even six-seven dollars, I would have to order in quantities approaching the millions. "You won't find that many kids with that kind of dough," one woodworker added philosophically.

Christmas was only ten days away. The orders and letters of inquiry piled up daily. "The only thing to do," Ginny said, "is return their checks and tell them that because of the unexpected rush of business you can't fill their orders. Or tell them you've run out of stock. Tell them *anything*. But stop wasting your time and losing money!"

"I can't tell them I'm out of stock," I said stubbornly. "I'm loaded with stock."

"You sure are," said Ginny. "You haven't even touched the pile in the attic. Another thing—do you realize what a fire hazard all those cardboard boxes are?"

I went back to the basement and worked harder than ever. Three or four of the neighbors and a brother-in-law pitched in and worked just as furiously. At first they took it as a lark, but after several hours of cutting around the same puppy-dog features and hammering nails almost too small to hold into exactly the same places, tempers grew edgy. A few highballs only made matters worse. Hammers began to hit thumbs, fingers got nicked on saw blades.

"Why the hell," said my brother-in-law at one point, "can't the little devils hang up their clothes like you and I used to do?"

At three in the morning wives started calling to find out if their husbands had forgotten they had homes of their own. Ginny came downstairs in her kimono, her face set in a sleepy, but grim, look that allowed no back talk.

"Those unfilled orders are going back tomorrow," she said.

"You're damn right," said my helpers. "Let's all have a nightcap and get to bed!"

The boys eventually discovered that the unused plywood was just the right thickness for making birdhouses and stations for their model railroad. The girls found the cardboard boxes perfect for school lunches. Even with a new box per lunch, the supply is still not exhausted. The only thing that even slightly annoys me is to hear one of the younger children, as she sets out for school, exclaim, "But, Daddy, what were all those boxes *for?*"

12 · Daddy Is a Dope

It was Sunday afternoon. In the red chair beside the fire-place, Ginny was reading the paper, in her first quiet moment since the usual Sunday round—church, breakfast, dishes, dinner and more dishes—had begun early that morning. In the dining room Tony and Tommy were straddling a chair apiece, waving toy pistols and taking pot shots at imaginary Indians. Upstairs the three oldest girls were sewing doll clothes; the two youngest were having their daily nap. Kip and Dave, who by now were determined to become farmers, were across the field helping Mr. Mason shear his sheep.

In spite of the cowboy yells from the dining room, the place was filled with that quiet peace that is so peculiar to comfortable Sunday afternoons. I was settling myself lazily before the television set, getting ready to enjoy a favorite program, which would be on the air in a few minutes. Every inch the tired warrior, I felt scarred and winded after a long week's bout with the typewriter, and this was my reward. Let no one disturb the hero's well-earned rest, I thought. I removed my tie and shoes.

"Tony," I called, during a lull in the nearby battle, "will you fetch Daddy his bedroom slippers?"

As he handed them to me, he half heartedly repeated the question he had been asking, with steadily diminishing hope all afternoon: "Won't you come down to the basement now and make the mountain for my train like you promised?"

"After a while," I told him, frowning. "Now will you be a good boy and turn on the television set?"

He sighed and said, "All right," and turned it on.

"Want me to pull the curtain?" he asked.

"Please."

The screen flickered and came alive with the smiling face of an attractive young woman. "You massage it in gently and you can almost *feel* those wrinkles disappear," said she who would have not a wrinkle for at least another ten years. "Youth and beauty can be yours if you follow this simple beauty treatment faithfully every bedtime." A seductive sweep of violin music covered her slow fade-out from the screen.

Tommy, the four year old, meanwhile had slid down from his chair and joined his older brother in front of the set.

"Is he going to make the mountain?" he whispered.

Tony shook his head. "Afterwhile—that's what he *said*."

"That's right, dear," I assured him.

"Only once in a great while," the announcer was saying, "is a television program privileged. . . ."

I was vaguely aware of a faint tapping sound outside the house, as if a tree branch was blowing against the wall.

". . . a play of such deep, penetrating human drama, a play that dares. . . ."

Whatever was making the noise was now tapping at the window, across which Tony had just drawn the curtains.

"What in the world is that?" Ginny asked.

"Tony," I said, "will you open the curtains and see what's out there?"

"It's a big piece of cardboard," Tony said, peering through the curtains.

"Open them up, will you, dear?" I asked him.

The cardboard was about two feet square and had been torn from the side of an old carton. It was suspended on a string, the other end of which, it wasn't hard to guess, was held by someone leaning out the attic window two stories above. But the cardboard itself did not startle me half as much as the message that had been scrawled across it in heavy black crayon. It said, "Daddy is a dope."

"What is it, dear?" Ginny asked from the red chair.

"Somebody's idea of a joke," I said, trying hard to think it was funny. "Those girls have sneaked up to the attic and lowered a message that says I'm a dope."

"*What?*" exclaimed Ginny.

"You're not a dope, Daddy," said Tommy, without taking his eyes off the television.

Ginny got up for a close look. She giggled, then laughed.

"If that's humor—" I began.

"Don't you *see?*" she said. "They want you to chase them."

"The scene," said the announcer's voice, "is London, 1789."

"*Who* wants me to chase them?"

"Who do you suppose? Kip and Dave, of course. The girls wouldn't call you a dope."

"I thought Kip and Dave were shearing sheep."

"They came back about fifteen minutes ago. Didn't you hear them creeping upstairs?"

"Why didn't you tell me?"

Her reply was drowned out by a burst of symphonic melody, appropriate, I suppose, to London, 1789.

I went back to my chair.

"Aren't you going to play with them?" Ginny asked, disappointed.

"I've waited all week to see this show."

"And they've waited all week to have some fun with you."

There was a clatter of hooves and the blare of a trumpet from the screen. A stagecoach pulled up before an old inn. The music faded.

"*Why* do they want me to chase them?" I asked, although I knew why. For the heck of it, of course.

"Is this the Sign of the Speckled Trout, driver?" asked a tired feminine voice from the bowels of the TV set.

"This is gonna be good," said Tony, hugging his knees. Like his brother, Kip, Tony considers anything good that has a horse in it somewhere.

The cardboard jiggled at the end of the string. "Well," it seemed to say, "are you just going to *sit* there?"

"Daddy is a dope," I muttered.

"Oh, Tim," said Ginny impatiently, "you *used* to chase them—remember?"

The "remember?" was whispered plaintively as if it was supposed to take me back at least seventy-five years.

"All right," I said reluctantly, getting up. "But just for a few minutes. And keep an eye on the show, will you, so you can fill me in when I get back?"

I tiptoed quietly up the stairs. I'd surprise them, scare the daylights out of them, and then get back to the television set, my duty to my children done.

"Where are you going?" Danielle asked, as I passed the bedroom where the girls were sewing.

"Shhh," I said.

Silently, they put down their work and tiptoed after me.

"Be careful of those attic steps," I whispered. "They squeak."

"But what's the matter?" insisted Nina.

"Nothing's the matter. I'm surprising the boys."

On the top landing, I opened the door to the attic and yelled, "Yaaah!" at full voice, expecting two surprised boys to collapse from shock.

But no one was in sight. The string supporting the cardboard had been fastened to the window latch.

"How do you like that?" I said. "Those two geniuses *knew* I'd come after them."

"Oh, goody," Peggy squealed, "now we'll *have* to find them."

Suddenly the room was filled with an ear-splitting shout. I jumped. From behind the door Kip's long arms encircled my neck and bent me over backwards. From a nearby closet Dave came charging like a slap-happy buffalo, and tackled me around my middle. I was borne to the floor amid a torrent of howls and challenges. "Thought you'd surprise us, eh?" . . . "Try and scare us now," they chortled.

"Let Daddy up!" the girls commanded. They leaped on top of the boys, adding their weight to the pile of bodies bearing down on me.

Time was when, in a harmless rough and tumble, I could handle both David and Kip with no strain. But even then I was amazed by their cheery unconcern about the outcome of the battles, as if they secretly knew it would not be long before these almost nightly tussles would have a different ending.

But gradually I found it wiser (more dignified, that is) to change my "Come on, you poor weaklings" to "Fair play, now boys. One at a time." It was with the reluctance of a man facing up to gray hair, shorter wind and an upper plate that I at last acknowledged the effectiveness of Kip's lean, fifteen-year-old muscles when pitted against my slightly older combination of muscles, fat, and unscientific method. ("You ought to watch wrestling on television," Kip advised.) I must take a few exercises and keep in trim for these birds, I told myself. "Play it smart and begin standing on your dignity," my older friends cautioned.

But dignity was pretty hard to stand on, with Kip's head-lock around my neck and David's bear hug around my waist, and the girls sitting on my legs one second and kissing my nose the next.

"Easy now," I panted. "Don't get me mad or I'll—"

Kip almost lost his hold with laughter. "You'll what?"

I reached out and grabbed what I thought was Dave's arm, and gave it a sharp twist to break its hold.

"Ouch!" cried Danielle, "you're hurting my leg." It soon became evident that the girls were not on my side any longer, but were helping the boys hold me down. It was more fun that way.

"Daddy can't get up!" they sang. "Daddy can't get up!"

But I did get up, to my everlasting credit. The twisting and turning finally placed both my legs against a door jamb so that I had leverage enough for a fierce backward thrust which caught both the boys off balance and sent them sprawling. The girls I disposed of with a piercing yell that scared them half out of their wits.

But as I struggled to my feet, my head rose above the window ledge and for one brief moment I had a fleeting glimpse of young Mrs. Lenning from next door standing open mouthed on the roadway behind her baby carriage. She was staring in horror at the window.

"Everything's okay!" I had time to call before Kip's arms again encircled my neck and dropped me from Mrs. Lenning's view.

When I broke free again, I plunged down the stairs with no loss of time, but strangely enough, I was hoping the children would chase me.

"You'll never catch me, you flat-footed elephants!" I challenged them.

"Oh, yeah?" they screamed, unbelieving. Daddy was actually playing with them.

I raced through the hall, into the kitchen, almost colliding with the worried Mrs. Lenning, who had just entered, holding her little Norbert in her arms. She gasped and leaped back as the rest of the stampede charged after me.

I swept out the back door, slamming it behind me. It would take them a second or two to fumble with the automatic catch, and that would give me time to race around the side of the house, push open a downstairs bedroom window and climb back in. Then I would sneak into the living room, where they would least expect to find me, and hide behind the couch.

The bedroom window went up easily, as I expected, but what I didn't expect was Mrs. Lenning removing little Norbert's leggings. Nor did Norbert expect to see me either. The sight of a man climbing in through the bedroom window, disheveled, panting, and with a pack of screaming children at his heels was too much for Norbert's infant nerves. He bellowed, white faced and terrified.

"Good heavens, Tim," Ginny scolded when she rushed into the room, "isn't this *overdoing* it?"

Mrs. Lenning picked up Norbert and patted him gently. With his head over her shoulder, he was pacified, but when he turned for another look, the panic returned.

"Now you've wakened Gael and Mary Jo," Ginny complained. "Listen to them!"

Upstairs one-year-old Gael was crying to be let out of her crib. Three-year-old Mary Jo was already padding down the stairs, sensing revelry.

I looked behind me. One of Kip's long legs was hooking itself over the window sill.

"Can't wait!" I panted, leaping for the door. "You know something?" I threw back over my shoulder. "This is fun!"

And it was—breathless, perspiring, red-faced fun, the kind I hadn't known since my days of cops and robbers.

I slipped in behind the couch and waited, the perspiration dropping on my hunched-up knees. The boys had climbed through the bedroom window, terrifying Norbert anew, but had evidently been sent retreating by Ginny. Now they circled the house hoping to catch me trying to escape from another exit.

The younger ones came back in. From the kitchen the girls shouted a theory that I had returned to the attic, and in a moment the sound of their stomping echoed up the stairs.

Tony came in and sat on the couch for a moment, then

suddenly said to himself, "He's down in the basement making my mountain," and raced off down the basement steps.

Finally there were slower, heavier footsteps across the living-room floor. Kippy, I thought, taking a breather. Letting the rest of the crowd do the work. Old Kip, the sly one. I'll fix *his* clock. When the footsteps were abreast of the couch, I leaped up, both arms waving and the walls rang with the resonance of my yell.

"God Almighty!" quavered Mr. Lenning, stumbling backward.

"Joe . . . " I murmured feebly.

Ginny ran into the room. "What in the world was *that?*"

"He scared the living hell out of me," Mr. Lenning panted, dropping his lanky frame into the nearest chair.

"I—I thought it was Kip," I murmured, as if that were my customary way of saluting my son.

"Tim," said Ginny, "what in the world has happened to you?"

"Hang it all," I said to Joe, "I was just having some fun with the kids, and I guess it got a little out of hand."

"I heard the excitement," said Joe Lenning, trying to puzzle it out in the light of pure reason, "So I came over to see if anything was wrong. It sounded like you were murdering somebody."

"It was the other way around," I said, with a small laugh. "Whatsay we calm down over a little drink?"

The children burst into the room one by one or in groups, only to be brought up short before the stunning fact that the game was at an end. They glared with undisguised hostility at our guests.

"We were chasing Daddy," Nina stated pointedly. "Were we having fun!"

"I think it's wonderful," said Mrs. Lenning, settling herself and Norbert on the couch.

"We were chasing Daddy," Tommy bubbled.

"That's all for a while, kids," I said. "Now you go back to what you were doing and let Daddy rest a bit."

For a few minutes the children milled around the room aimlessly like mourners at a graveside after the final prayers have been said. Then Nina, Danielle and Peggy reluctantly returned to their doll clothes. Kip and David wandered outside. Gael by now was gurgling contentedly in her playpen. Tony and Tommy and Mary Jo sat on the floor before the television screen, where London, 1789, had been switched off in favor of a juggler, 1954. "The horses were gone anyway," said Tony.

The rest of the afternoon slipped away in a tinkle of highball glasses, small talk, and an occasional glance at the television set.

"I'll lock up," I said to Ginny that night. "Why don't you turn in? It's been a long day."

She was staring bemused at the floor in front of the television set, where Tony, Tommy and Mary Jo had spent most of the evening. "Tim," she said, "we have to give them more time. More time having fun."

"We will," I promised largely.

"All they really want is *us*."

"I suppose you're right."

"If you could have seen their faces when you were playing with them."

"If you could have seen *your* face when I was playing with them."

"Oh, I know I have a lot to learn. I'm far from perfect."

Not too far, I thought; I never cease to marvel at her

ability to meet with infinite patience the persistent squalling,
bawling, tripping, bumping, bruising, falling, complaining,
interrupting, dressing and undressing, the peremptory com-
mands, the whining complaints: "Zip me up, Mummy" . . .
"Tommy hit me" . . . "She hit me first" . . . "I fell in the
pool" . . . "The door won't open" . . . "I can't find my
shoes" . . . "I can't button this" . . . "I don't *want* to take
a nap today."

If I'm well rested, without too many things to worry or
fret about, I can weather this daily storm for about an hour
or two without trimming my sails, but if the weather continues
to worsen, or my nerves are not in their best operating condition, I either head for the nearest port, a quiet corner of the
house if such can be found, or I shout orders in such Captain-
Bligh fashion that for a while at least I keep all hands in pop-
eyed silence.

Ginny, however, will occasionally lose her temper and demand to know how she can be expected to stand all this
another minute. When the other minute comes around, she is
patiently helping Mary Jo find a lost dolly and addressing her
as "My little treasure."

After Ginny had gone upstairs, I tried the doors, turned
off the lights in the kitchen and dining room, and went into the
living room to close the curtains. In the half-glow of the one
lamp I had left still burning, the piece of cardboard was
visible through the glass, swinging and twisting erratically in
the rising wind. The words did a merry dance. "Daddy is a
dope."

Time enough to take it down in the morning, I said to myself. I was dead tired. My back muscles ached. How swiftly
the boys grow tall and strong, I thought, remembering the

powerful vice of Kip's arms around my neck, and David's wild charge into my midsection.

Eleven o'clock at night in a house quiet with the sleep of many children is a treacherous hour. The downstairs rooms are too suddenly empty, too suddenly still. Your sense of aloneness is too sharp. Your thoughts turn in upon themselves and you begin examining your conscience in a mood shaded by the darkness outside. Why had I felt so elated over the few minutes spent playing with the kids? Own up to it. Because, I told myself, you are not used to it. You have not given them enough of yourself.

"All they want is us."

Snap out of this, I said. Get to bed; get some sleep. Nobody can accuse *you* of not being a good parent.

"Daddy, won't you come down in the basement and help me make a mountain for my train like you promised?" Emphasis on the "promised," the hopeful appeal to the high court of adult honor.

My father, now, had been a wise man. No staying up late at night in an empty house for him. Even for company. Came ten o'clock and he was ready for bed. If guests lingered, they were promptly sent on their way by a polite remark made to my mother: "Mary," my father would say, slapping the arms of his chair, closing all "quotes" for the evening, "we'd better let these people get home and get their rest."

No eleven o'clock examinations of conscience. He *knew* he was a good father. Never a Christmas without more toys than I expected. Never a birthday without a big fuss. But more important, never a trip to the store without an invitation to come along; never a repair job around the house without the opportunity to hold the hammer and nails; never a

walk through the yard or a vacant lot without a dare to hit
that tree with a pebble in three tries.

And those are the moments of childhood I remember best.

As I crawled into bed, I thought, "Why do mothers seem
to understand these things so well?"

I was suddenly back to one night in the early, apartment
days of our marriage, when Kip, a few months old, slept in
his bassinet in the living room. It was two o'clock in the
morning. The baby had just been fed, burped, and changed—
by Ginny.

And yet he was crying. I lay in bed hoping one more minute
or two would see him drop off to sleep. But the crying kept
on.

"Well," I admitted grudgingly, "I guess it's my turn to
get up."

I lifted him, tried to burp him some more. He was quiet,
even happy, while I held him, but howled the moment I laid
him down. Damnation, I thought, a fellow can't sit here all
night holding a baby. I put him back, a little roughly, I
suppose, for his crying took on a new note of fear.

Don't spoil him, I told myself. Let him cry it out.

There was a whisper of feet in the little hallway, and the
tall, nightgowned figure of Ginny, wraithlike in the darkness,
bent over the bassinet, and with a warm, mothering gesture
of enfoldment, lifted Kip in her arms. The crying stopped.

"What in the world is the matter with him?" I groused.

"He's lonesome, that's all. He wants *us*." It seemed as if
she had known exactly what to do from the day she was born.
With the baby tight against her shoulder, she started for the
bedroom.

"Now wait a minute," I said. I had read somewhere that parents were entitled to their night of undisturbed sleep.

Ginny continued into the bedroom.

"Are we going to make a habit of this?" I grumbled as I got into bed beside my infant son, who was waving his arms and kicking his legs in pure delight.

"He won't be lonesome *every* night," Ginny reassured me. "He just has to *know* we love him."

I had not yet discovered that a man may become a husband in a day, but that fatherhood is a thing of degrees, and some men grow into it slowly.

Yes, I told myself, as my thoughts of the past grew foggy with sleep, I guess I can safely say I've learned a lot since then.

Suddenly there was a familiar noise at the bedroom door. Four-year-old Tommy again, soundlessly tiptoeing his pudgy way across the floor to Ginny's side of the bed, and softly patting the pillow beside her head to let her know gently that he was there. His trick was to slip in quietly beside his mother without disturbing his father, who, if awakened, would pick him up promptly and in no uncertain terms plant him firmly back in his own bed.

But tonight I held still. "Tommy," I whispered, "come over here with Daddy."

I heard the tiny gasp of surprise.

"Come on, dear," I said.

The "dear" did it. No mistaking my intentions now. He fairly raced around the end of the bed.

His blonde head buried itself cozily in the folds of the bedclothes. But he felt some apology was called for.

"There's a lion in my closet," he said, and almost at once dropped off to sleep.

The wind was rising. It whistled through the tree branches near the window and hummed a monotone in the weather-stripping of the open window. So a parent is entitled to a night of undisturbed rest, is he? I asked smugly. He's also entitled to the rich, intimate experience of having a small son snuggle down beside him, warm and peaceful with his great feeling of security, and the night wind blowing outside.

"I slept with Daddy last night," Tommy proudly told the others next morning.

The following night, he came back. The lion was still in his closet, it seemed. Half an hour later Tony joined him. "There's a bear under my bed." The wild animals have certainly taken over, I thought, but let's be patient.

Next night the original two were increased to three. Mary Jo had heard a man under her bed. Anyway, I muttered, that's a twist.

When, two nights later, seven-year-old Peggy, who was much too old for this sort of thing, I thought, crept in, I drew the line. I calculated rapidly that this would make a total of six people in the same bed. Enough's enough.

"Look," I said firmly, "you're all going back to your own beds. There are no lions and no men in your rooms."

"There was a big bird in mine," Peggy defended herself.

"Bird or no bird, you're going back."

I turned on the lights in their rooms, carefully opened their closet doors to convince them there was no wild life present. They all soberly peered in to make sure.

"What's the matter, dear?" Ginny stage whispered from the next room, half awake.

"We're looking for lions," I whispered back.

"There aren't any," she said matter-of-factly, and went back to sleep.

"What are we going to do with those kids?" I asked her next morning.

"We have to be with them more," she said. "That's all."

It's a big order, but as yet I haven't thought of a substitute.

13 · You Gotta Be Firm

Discipline, naturally, is of prime importance, as it is in any segment of society composed of certain individuals who, by nature, tend to act as if they're doing you a favor by accepting the shelter, food and clothing you provide.

How do you impress a rambunctious fourteen-year-old boy with the importance of hanging up towels after he has used them, or of making his bed every morning and not just once a week, or of showing up promptly for dinner?

And when he fails, how do you discipline him?

How do you discipline a seven-year-old girl who "forgets" almost every night to put her bicycle under cover? Or to come directly home from school instead of stopping at a girl friend's house and calling you up at six o'clock to say she has been invited to stay for dinner?

"Discipline," wrote one sage, "must not be a hit-or-miss affair, reflecting nothing more constructive than the parents' moods. It must be administered dispassionately, though firmly, and above all, threats of punishment should not be made unless you intend to enforce them."

Now this is sound advice, and no thinking parent would take it lightly, even though I suspect the expert was writing from his rose garden with the sun warming his back, a cool drink at his elbow, the bluebirds singing from beyond the fountain, and his children, if any, away with Grandma for an outing at the South Pole.

My trouble has always been that my threats not only reflect my moods, but are the direct product of my moods. They may range from a mild "Don't blow that whistle again, dear, or I'll take it away from you" to a ferocious "One more surly remark from *you*, young man, and I'll knock your block off." By the time I get around to putting my threats into action, however, my mood has improved considerably, as witnessed by the fact that my children, at this writing, still have their blocks fixed firmly to their shoulders.

The most common cause for annoyance at our house is the older boys' attitude that nothing is too good for their horses, including meals of freshly planted petunias, with roughage nibbled from the trunks of our best-producing fruit trees. ("A fellow can't remember to lock the pasture gate *every* night, can he, Dad?")

What if the faucet at the watering trough *isn't* always turned off in the evening, and the well pump has to work at top speed right through the following dawn? Isn't it better for the boys to forget to turn it off than to neglect to turn it on? How would I like it if the horses went thirsty all night?

And don't worry about the stable, Dad; we forgot to

clean it out the last two weeks, but we sure won't forget today. The stable, it should be noted, is one half of the two-car garage, the car, oddly enough, being allowed to occupy the other half. Unless the floor is cleaned at least twice a week, the car interior, even with the windows closed, assumes the aroma of the Augean stables before Ulysses got busy on them, a condition not easy to explain to acquaintances riding with me for the first time.

"Horses," I tell them, as they hastily roll down the nearest window.

"You should make the horses get out and walk," the more humorous passengers reply. "The exercise would do them good."

Compared to our pampered pets, the sacred cows of India are excommunicated heretics.

How often have I scolded, cajoled, threatened? "So you used the porch awning to cover the new hay, did you?"

"Well, gosh, Dad, you wouldn't want the hay to get all wet, would you?"

For such serious offenses as this—which occurred during a severe winter—I reserve the master threat of all. "Listen," I tell them fiercely, "those horses will have to go. They're becoming too big a nuisance, y'understand?"

The boys respond by thrusting their hands deep in their pockets and considering their shoe tops for what I once supposed was an agonizing minute. I learned later, however, that they were merely rolling with the punch. "Okay," I clinch it, "we're getting rid of them, since you obviously don't know how to take care of them. There'll be an ad for two horses in next Sunday's paper."

Usually, there *is* an ad for two, and oftentimes more, horses in Sunday's paper, but to date, the horses have not been ours. By Friday evening, which is the deadline for placing a Sunday ad, the boys and I are planning our spring fishing trips, and how can you sell horses out from under two fellow fishermen?

For about a week after my blowups the horses become as unobtrusively well behaved as the sub-deacon at Solemn High Mass. But then, gradually, the garage floor becomes thick with accumulated manure, and stretches of freshly seeded lawn are once again pock-marked with the hoofprints of careless short cuts.

"The trouble is," Ginny says, backing up the experts one-hundred percent, "you never follow through on any of your threats, and the boys know it."

At last, however, I followed through.

By the corner of the pasture fence nearest the house, where the fence runs up within a few feet of the stable-garage, then turns at right angles and retreats northward, there is a spot which I always thought would be perfect for a planting of shrubs and trees.

"A few spreading fitzers," I explained to Ginny one day, "a tall juniper or two; then, topping the whole thing off, a cluster of two or three white birch trees."

"It sounds wonderful," she said, "but won't the horses get to them?"

"Not if we string some extra runners of barbed wire along the top of the fence. I've seen it done lots of times. Very effective."

"Well," said Ginny, "if you're sure."

Of course I was sure. My faith in barbed wire had been unshakable since the day when, building the original pasture fence, I dropped a roll of it down my leg and had to have

several stitches taken in both my pants and myself to repair
the damage.

To the planting of the birches, my favorite tree, I gave
special attention. I visited several nurseries to find exactly
the specimens I wanted, two trunks to a root, tall, and as
gracefully tipped as a peacock's feather; and had carefully
noted every scrap of the nurseryman's advice on how to plant
them. The holes were dug to exactly the right size, the right
proportion of loose soil and fertilizer was carefully mixed,
the right amount of water lovingly poured in, and the ground
tamped firmly about the roots to squeeze out any air pockets.

I called Ginny for the final approval.

"They're beautiful," she said, surveying the upper reaches
of the twelve-foot-high birches. "But the horses—?"

"I'm not finished yet," I assured her. "Kip! Dave!" I
called.

The boys hurried out from the house where they had become absorbed in television about the time I started to
dig.

"Now comes *your* part of the job," I told them, and explained exactly what I wanted them to do. "Good solid boards,
see? About three feet long. Angle them in toward the pasture
and nail them to the top of these four fence posts. Then
string them tight with several strands of barbed wire, get
it?"

They nodded their heads in complete approval and understanding, then disappeared into the basement in search of
wood, nails, hammer and wire.

For half an hour, while I relaxed in the living room with
a glass of beer, the air was filled with the reassuring sounds of
their pounding.

At dusk, they came back to the house, proud of their job, detailing every step of the project. "That fence would hold back an elephant," David boasted.

"Don't you think you'd better inspect it?" Ginny asked me.

The boys looked hurt. "She doesn't think we can do *anything*," they complained.

"Nonsense," I told her. "They say they've done a good job, so they've done it."

But just to be sure, I sauntered out to the pasture after the boys had gone to bed, and as well as I could with a flashlight, determined that the wire was exactly where I had told them to put it.

When I awoke next morning, I went to the bedroom window, still in my pajamas, to make sure the wire had held. Ginny, still asleep, promptly awoke, however, at the sound of my choked cry. "The trees! The horses!" I was incoherent. Flinging open the window I leaned out in the hysterical hope that if there were no glass in front of me the scene would change.

Ginny leaped from bed and rushed to my side. There in the misty light of the wet spring morning, with the birds singing more happily, and the first daffodils blooming more vigorously than they had since the days of Creation, stood the two horses, their necks wreathed in garlands of barbed wire, their big stupid faces glowing with the paradisiac satisfaction that can only follow a breakfast of tender young birches. Of trees that once stood twelve feet high, all that was left were humiliated, ragged-tipped stubs that measured no higher than a short man's waist.

My yell for the boys awoke the whole household. In bathrobes and slippers we streamed out to the fence.

"Dammit all!" I shouted over my shoulder, "what did you put those boards and that wire up with—thumb tacks?"

"We couldn't find the big nails or the staples," one of them quavered. "So we used those old roofing nails."

"Roofing nails! What in the devil have I done to deserve such feeble-minded offspring!"

The horses tossed their heads and whinnied in fear. With each movement the wire barbs pricked their necks and made them more panicky.

"Tim," said Ginny, "why didn't you make *sure* the fence was all right?"

I waved my arms helplessly.

"We gotta get that wire off them," David gulped.

The horses were rising up on their hind legs, snorting and pawing the air as if posing for Rosa Bonheur.

Expertly, Kip and Dave slipped them free of the wire and chased them out of range, not however, before I planted a solid kick on the flanks of one, sailing my bedroom slipper twenty feet farther into the rain-soaked pasture. Without a word David retrieved it, while I stood on one foot fuming.

Eventually, I got the hedge clippers out of the garage, and while I made the futile gesture of restoring some kind of symmetry to the frayed birches, the rest of the family slipped quietly back to the house.

When I returned to the kitchen, I called the boys, who had hidden, I supposed, under their beds. White faced, pop eyed, they came downstairs again, and stood miserably waiting their judgment.

"Okay," I said grimly, "I've threatened this before, but never followed through. Today, I'm following through. I'm placing an ad in next Sunday's paper for those horses right now!"

I reached for the telephone, but realized I should give some thought to composing the ad—an ad that would sell.

"What do you say," I asked Ginny, "when you want to unload a couple of dumb nags on some poor unsuspecting buyer?"

Ginny found a pencil. "Let's see," she said cooperatively, tearing a margin from a magazine to write on. "Registered Morgan mare," she composed, "five years old—"

"Witless, stupid and dangerous," I grunted.

"You can't say that," she interrupted. "Five years old, beautiful chestnut."

"I'm hanged if I'll call that tree-eating monster beautiful."

"Well, she *is* beautiful," Ginny insisted. "You've said so yourself several times."

"I must have been out of my mind."

The muscles in Kip's jaw were working furiously. "She sure is," he sputtered.

"None of that now," I warned.

"Beautiful chestnut," she wrote. "Very gentle."

"Especially when full of fresh birch."

"Very gentle. Raised with children."

"And obviously a bad influence on them."

"Now for David's horse."

David turned on his heel and rushed upstairs to his room.

"Okay," I said sternly. "David's horse."

"Five-year-old pinto mare," said Ginny. "Part quarter horse, part Arabian. Even tempered." She thought for a moment. "No," she said, crossing the last reference out, "I'll save the 'raised with children' till the last, and that will cover both of them."

"Very good," I said, and picked up the phone.

The adtaker had a suggestion. For practically the same rate, I could also run an ad in Saturday's paper, too.

"Fine," I said. "Saturday *and* Sunday." I read them Ginny's brief panegyric, saying the words "beautiful" and "gentle" with considerable difficulty.

Without looking at Kip or his mother, I grumbled, *"Now who makes threats he can't enforce?"* I stomped upstairs, assuring myself that harsh as I must have seemed I was acting entirely within my parental rights. In fact it was my duty to be firm. The angels were definitely on my side. Hadn't even the angels resorted to violence on occasion? What about the Cherubim and the flaming sword at the gates of Paradise, and that one that wrestled Jonah?

I glanced out the bathroom window when I started to shave and noticed Kip, still in his bathrobe, sitting on Tony's old coaster wagon down beside the pasture fence, gazing vacantly at the horses, and absently drawing a few long strands of hay through his fingers. I pulled down the shade.

That day, after the boys came home from school, they quietly assigned themselves certain chores without a word from their mother or me. They curried and brushed their horses, which were shedding their heavy winter coats, and carefully swept up the combings from the garage floor. They fed them an extra helping of oats and corn, and instead of riding them as they did each day, returned them to the pasture.

Then they cleaned up around the feed bins so that not a grain was visible.

They emptied the garbage from the kitchen, making sure that none of it spilled. They burned papers and watered the new evergreens.

During dinner they were subdued and overly polite. They avoided speaking to me as much as possible and directed most of their remarks to Ginny. They were halfway upstairs before they said good-night.

Next day, David found time after school to wash the car, and Kip cleaned and oiled the lawnmower. At bedtime David screwed up enough courage to tell me he had pitched three innings in a school game that noontime and had struck out four batters. But he didn't wait for my comment. Instead, he immediately turned his full attention to showing Tommy how to stand on his head.

Earlier that day, in hopes that the trees might still be saved, I had called up the nurseryman for advice.

"So you have horses," he said.

"We do," I answered, "though it won't be for long."

"My boy is always after me to buy him a horse," sighed the nurseryman, "but I can't afford it."

"Neither can I," I said, "especially on a diet of young birches." I told him what had happened.

"Oh, don't worry about the trees," he laughed. "As long as you trimmed them clean they'll be okay."

"You mean it?"

"Sure. In fact, they'll grow up stronger than ever. Say," he added with unnecessary frivolity, "why don't you try feeding those horses hay and stuff like that?" His rustic guffaws were still sounding in the receiver when I hung up.

The following day was Saturday. David, as usual, the first of the children to get dressed, went outside, and brought in the morning paper. He opened it as nonchalantly as possible on the dining-room table, pretended to read the funnies, but worked his way steadily to the ads at the back. I was busy spooning up cereal and pretended not to notice.

Suddenly there was the sound of the paper being folded up, and David came back to the breakfast room. His hand rested for a moment on my shoulders, and as he slid happily into his chair, he gave me an awkward, wobbly pat. Then, with familiar gusto, he addressed himself to his breakfast.

That afternoon, after a trip to the mailbox, he informed me with a hopeful smile, that the special-size horse shoes he had ordered a week before were up at the post office waiting for two dollars and thirty cents C.O.D.

"Who'll put them on?" I asked.

The farmer next door had said he would do the job.

"Okay," I said, giving him the money.

Before dinner, David and his brother were galloping down the lane past our front window.

"Wasn't the ad supposed to run in this morning's paper?" Ginny asked suspiciously.

"I didn't check," I said truthfully.

She eyed me with the mock severity of the woman who knows all along exactly what her husband will do next.

"You cancelled it," she accused.

There was no point in denying it. "The cancellation number is on the back of the telephone directory," I said boldly.

"The trouble with you—" she began, then kissed me.

"I know," I said, "but my mood changed."

14 · The Rest Will Do You Good

The night was raw and blustery, with furious little twisters of rain and snow doing a December dance on every corner. Up ahead the wet pavement sparkled with the reflected gymnastics of lights on an all-night movie-house marquee. An illuminated patch of sidewalk in front of a store window blinked out in answer to a time clock's summons. Above a tavern doorway an animated neon cocktail glass bubbled an invitation to come in and forget your troubles. I refused the invitation because I had already been in and my troubles were not forgotten.

The biggest trouble of all was that I was hundreds of miles from sight or sound of my wife and children, whom I hadn't seen for a week. And although I was going home soon, I was lonesome, and growing more lonesome by the minute.

It was no night, or time, for a stroll, but my hotel room had grown unbearably small; I had seen the best movie in town twice already, and since I couldn't sleep, I decided to take a walk.

I am sometimes envied my occupation as a writer for a commercial motion picture producer, because many out-of-town assignments give me periodic opportunities to "get away from it all."

For a while before each trip, I even try to agree that a few days on my own will do me a lot of good, whatever that means. But as the time for departure approaches, usually in the evening for an overnight train ride, it becomes increasingly apparent that I won't be getting away from a thing.

The saddening, though flattering, sight of the kids' faces, doleful over the thought of losing their daddy, will stick with me for days, and by that time my own face will have grown doleful from thinking of what *I* have lost.

For hours before I leave, the younger ones come to me, one by one, hold onto my arm and lament, "I *wish* you didn't have to go." I answer, "I wish so, too, but don't worry, I'll be back in a day or two."

"That's what you said last time, but you were gone for two weeks!"

The drive to the station is like a drive to a cemetery. Ginny chauffeurs, accompanied by Kip. David stays home to watch over the others.

We don't say much, except that I appoint Kip the man of the house in my absence and charge him with the responsibility of locking all downstairs doors at night—which, of course, he will forget to do because he doesn't see the point of it. Why would anyone want to get into *our* house?

On the train I try to put my family completely out of my mind, but I find it impossible to do so. Because I keep thinking how much fun it would be to sit in the lounge car with Kip and Dave over a coke. Wouldn't Tony and Tommy love the excitement of pulling out of the station—the "all aboard," the last-minute scurrying of the redcaps, the blinking of the signal lights as we slip out of the yards?

I go to bed—"Imagine," I can hear Danielle saying, "actually sleeping in a *bed* on a *train!*"

And breakfast—actually eating at a *table* on a *train*—as the countryside flows past, and the suburban stations flash by, with the commuters looking up from their papers and possibly wishing they were where you are; and then the sights of a strange, new city as they envelop you, the crawl into the station, the banging of vestibule doors, the porters calling the redcaps. And the long walk up past the head-end, where the big diesel sits that pulled you through the night; and the engineer, leaning out the window of his cab, waiting for some little boy to come along he can wave to.

No, a train is no place to forget children.

You keep your mind pretty well on business during the working day, but in the evening, when the people you have been calling on are leaving for their homes and families, you return to your hotel room, wash up, sit for a minute over the paper before going out to dinner.

What are *they* doing about now?

Well, Ginny is calling the boys in to clean up, the girls are helping her set the table. Peggy has placed Gael Marie in her high chair and is feeding her. In a moment David will light the candles on the dining-room table and Ginny will warn him not to play with the matches. They'll all sit down, Peggy will remind them, "We forgot grace," and they'll say their prayers with Tony ten words behind confusing everybody. And at the head of the table—but enough!

So you have your dinner alone, see a movie, have a nightcap, and although it's no night for walking, you walk.

Suddenly, as you turn a corner and head back for the hotel, you see something that makes you stop.

A shop—"Aunt Martha's Style Parade"—still lighted, and a white-haired old lady, presumably Aunt Martha, busy redoing her window. But it's what's *in* the window that makes you pause—dresses. Little girls' dresses, sizes three through twelve. Bright, fluffy dresses, as if made of snowflakes, pink and blue and white, with crinoline bows like little wings.

And above the dresses I think I see faces.

I tap on the window and point to a dress that seems made for Mary Jo. Aunt Martha looks startled; her lips purse suspiciously at sight of this muffled stranger with the dripping hat brim.

"No, dear," she mouths through the glass. "We're closed."

She's a kindly old lady, however, and as she sees my look of disappointment, she adds, "But we'll be open tomorrow at nine."

But I can't make it tomorrow, I tell her; I'll be too busy. I point once again to the dress. "It'll only take a minute."

She glances nervously at a nursery clock on display, but it's not much help; it says five-thirty.

She shakes her head finally, as if giving in, and parting the dresses in front of her like a hunter moving through tall grass, she comes to the door and opens the lock.

"We really open tomorrow at nine," she says once more, but she has swung the door back, and I step inside.

"I really shouldn't be doing this," she explains, turning the lock after me, "but we're so busy lately, I just never get a chance to fix my window."

"I won't be a minute," I assure her. "It's that little pink one I want, with the white top and the black ribbon around the middle."

"Oh, that's a beautiful dress," she says, lifting it tenderly off its stand. "How old is your little girl?"

"Just three." I see Mary Jo's big dimples above the dress.

"Big for her age?" she asks.

"I wouldn't say so. Let's see, she's about this high."

She studies my outstretched hand and holds the dress beneath it. Quickly I raise my hand to the right height for the dress. "Perfect," I say.

But how can I bring a dress home to Mary Jo without one for Peggy? After all, though she's only seven, Peggy is still a baby, isn't she?

"How about that white one with the pink bows?"

Aunt Martha looks more startled than before. "But that's a size seven."

"Perfect," I say. "I'll take that one, too."

Her hand flutters to her throat. "Oh," she says, "you mean you have another daughter?"

"Exactly." I see Peggy's smile, with its missing baby teeth, above the collar.

Two dresses. Not a bad armload of gifts to come home with, I feel. But then—how will Danielle and Nina react?

Sure they've grown up—nine and twelve—or *is* twelve so grown up. And if I have my doubts about twelve, what about nine?

While Aunt Martha is wrapping up the two dresses, I examine my wallet. There's never as much in it as I think there is, but there's enough for another dress or two. Of course, somewhere in this stange city I'll have to cash a check tomorrow to take me home, but at the moment tomorrow presents no problems.

"Now then," I say, "if you don't mind, could I look at that one with all the blue?"

Aunt Martha looks out the window, hoping, I'm sure, to see a policeman going by. But there is no one around. Only the two of us.

"Certainly," she says weakly. She almost runs to get the dress. If this is a holdup, the sooner it's over the better.

"That's beautiful," I say. I can see Danielle's long blonde hair above the blue.

Aunt Martha nods dumbly and turns back to the counter.

"Before you wrap it up—" I start to say.

"Oh, no, dear," she pipes. "No, no!"

"It's all right," I reassure her. "Actually I have *five* daughters. But the baby's too young to care whether I bring her anything or not."

"Five daughters?" This is happy news, but can she be sure? After all, it's late at night; it's storming outside and— five daughters. Well!

Aunt Martha works furiously now, throwing me an occasional frantic smile to keep me at bay until she can get the packages wrapped and me out the door.

But from the corner of the shop something bright red, with gold buttons, catches my eye. A baby boy's plaid waistcoat! The very thing for Tony! How could I forget Tony?

Aunt Martha sees me fingering it, but pretends not to notice. Her fingers fly, the swirls of ribbon flashing like Fourth-of-July sparklers waved in the dark.

"It'll be just a second," she breathes.

"I was just wondering," I say, "if you might have another of these, just a size smaller." How could I forget Tommy?

Aunt Martha throws another hopeful, agonized glance at the front window, but there is only the rain and snow outside.

"You—you have boys, too?"

"Four of them to be exact."

"Nine children!" She knows I'm lying! *Nobody* has nine children. Isn't the national average somewhere around two or three?

Yes, she has another waistcoat all right, but she is trembling now. The blow must fall any minute. There are no more children to stall around with.

I know how agitated she must be, and I do my best to put her at ease, but each attempt only convinces her the more that I'm a lunatic. Imagine, buying clothes for all those children in the middle of the night!

At last she adds up the bill, which takes almost every cent I have; and after I pay her, she opens the door, standing well behind it for protection. Her eyes are wary as if expecting another child to pop up any minute.

My heels are hardly across the threshold before the door closes, the lock clicks, and the lights go out.

Loaded down like Santa Claus, I make my way up the dark street, tired, wet, but very happy. I am carrying six of my nine children in my arms.

A squad car cruises up beside me at the curb and slows down. A ruddy Irish face peers at me suspiciously.

"Where y'goin', Mac?"

"Back to my hotel," I answer. "I was just taking a walk."

The squad car stops.

"What y'got there?"

"Clothes for my kids," I tell him. I do an expert job of

juggling the packages while I fish in my pocket for Aunt
Martha's receipt. "See? Just bought 'em at Aunt Martha's.
She opened up for me."

"God Almighty," he says, "how many kids y'got?"

"Nine," I say, and for once the number seems ridiculous.

But not to the policeman. "I thought *I* was good," he says,
nudging his partner beside him. "But I only got seven."

"Get in," says the other, "and we'll drive you back to the
hotel. This is a helluva night for a guy with nine kids to be
out."

"Believe me," I told Ginny when I returned (and we discovered to everyone's amazement, including my own, that the
dresses fit perfectly), "Next time I go anywhere, the kids
are going, too."

"Not *all* of them! How would you manage?"

"Maybe not all of them, but a lot of them."

"But wouldn't *I* have to go, too?" Ginny asked quietly.
"Who'd take care of the others?"

"Who'd take care of the ones with you?" she countered.

"Now *that's* a nice thing to say."

"I mean during the day, when you're busy with your work."

I hadn't thought of that. But I thought of it now, and the
vision of Kip, Dave, Nina and Danielle and one or two of
the smaller ones sitting in on a business conference was not
reassuring.

"You're right," I admitted glumly. "It's no use."

"Unless *I* came along," Ginny smiled.

"What are you driving at?"

"We could get someone to stay with the others, and
couldn't we make it a sort of vacation instead of a business
trip? You haven't had any time off in I don't know how long."

I knew how long, and just thinking of it made me tired.

"You think we could?"

Just imagining that we could get someone to stay with some of the children, or that I could take a vacation during one of the busiest times of the year indicated a boldness of thought that would have done credit to the planners of the Normandy Invasion.

But the more we thought about it, the more plausible it became. A cousin of Ginny's had just heard from a friend of hers about a wonderful woman who said she kept herself young by managing households during the parents' absence. We interviewed her, and found her to be even nicer than we expected. Most important of all, she loved children, and didn't care how many we left in her charge.

The next question was when, exactly, should we go? Our substitute mother narrowed the possibilities by telling us she had only a certain week available during the month of April.

"What days?" asked Kip. She told him.

"My spring vacation!" Kip was in high school.

This made it pretty evident that he, at least, would go, providing I could arrange *my* time to fit the same dates.

But like the waters of the Red Sea parting for the Israelites, my month's schedule of work, with a little maneuvering here and there, opened obligingly and let us pass.

Who, besides Kip, would go?

"Me," said David. "I could get a week off if I did extra work."

"Me," said Nina. "I could get off too."

"Me, me, me," the others chorused.

"Judging by your bad grammar," I said sternly, "none of you can afford to be away from school one minute."

It was finally decided, however, that as long as Kip was

definitely going, the logical thing would be to take his next oldest brother, so David won out, much to the consternation of the girls.

"Don't worry," Ginny told them. "You're going next time."

To me she said, "After all, this is only the beginning. We're going to get some fun out of life."

When I considered how easily all obstacles to the present trip had dissolved, I merely nodded. Maybe this *would* be only the beginning.

For me the trip would be strictly a vacation, but for the boys, as we assured David's teacher, it would be an educational vacation. We picked Washington, D.C., as the first stop, principally because I love to go there, and Ginny's only experience with our nation's capital had come from my enthusiastic descriptions of it, and because the boys' experience had been limited to what they could read in history books. It would be wonderful, we felt, to give them a first-hand knowledge of the great centers of interest that up to now had been only words and pictures on a page.

Then we would go to New York, Ginny's favorite city, to ride the ferry, climb the Statue of Liberty, visit the U.N., take in a show or two, and meet one or more of her relatives living there.

I was not disappointed in the stimulating effect the train ride to Washington produced on the boys. It was their first experience in overnight travel, and they spent nearly the whole time lifting the shade to see where we were, lowering the shade to get some sleep, then immediately raising it again for fear they were missing something.

A near fight in the corridor outside our room between two inebriated travelers and the porter, who was trying to pacify them, gave the whole thing a "life-is-real, life-is-earnest" flavor that greatly impressed the boys.

At breakfast I tried to build their anticipation for Washington by painting a thumb-nail sketch of some of the historical points of interest.

"Just imagine," I said, "you'll see the White House, the place where our presidents live . . . where Abraham Lincoln lived, where—"

"Yeah, that's right," said Kip. "Say," he asked, "did you *hear* those guys last night threaten to beat up the porter?"

"And you'll see the Smithsonian Institution," I went ahead doggedly, "where they keep the Wright brothers' first plane. Just think—"

"They didn't actually *hit* the porter," Dave interrupted, to keep the records on the fight clear. "But do you know what one of them said?"

"No," I said firmly, "and I'm not interested."

"But, gee, it was terrific."

Sporadically, the boys were still discussing the fight when we arrived in Washington. Only when they caught that first, breath-taking view of the capitol dome, framed by the arches of the station portico, were they quieted.

"Boy," said David in awe, "is that something!"

"It sure is," said Kip.

On the last of our three days in the city, after tramping through the White House, the House of Representatives, the Smithsonian, the U.S. Mint, the National Art Galleries, the Lincoln Memorial, and a dozen other highspots, Kip wrote Tony a postcard, which he handed me to mail. Curious, I glanced at the message to see what experience had made the biggest impression.

"Dear Tony," it began, "you should have seen the fight we saw on the train to Washington. . . ."

In New York we turned our time over completely to the boys and did everything they had ever heard was worth doing. We climbed the Statue of Liberty, rode to the top of the Empire State Building, saw two big ocean liners dock, went out to the Bronx Zoo and otherwise followed our sons around.

On the evening of the last day, Ginny and I decided to go to a play, a plan which the boys did not relish. They preferred to stay in their room, and watch one of their favorite television broadcasts.

"They must be tired," Ginny said. "I think they need the rest."

I got my first inkling that the boys weren't so awfully tired when I called at the desk for the key to our room.

"Quite some boys you have there," the clerk said, but his tone of voice was not entirely complimentary.

"Anything wrong?" I asked.

"Oh, nothing serious," he said. "It's all been ironed out."

"But what happened?"

"Nothing really, just a little excitement over a toy they had in their room."

"A toy?"

"Perhaps," he suggested, "it would be better if the boys told you themselves."

"Those kids have been up to something," I sputtered to Ginny in the elevator. "I *knew* we shouldn't have left them alone."

I knocked on the boys' door. There was no response; they

were sound asleep and refused to be wakened. Further pounding would only disturb the other guests on the floor. So we went into our own room and called them on the phone. "Open your door," I said curtly. "I want to talk to you!"

Half-awake, entirely out of sympathy with this late-hour cross-examination, they yawned, gave disconnected, sleepy answers, ran their fingers through their hair, leaned back on the bed and dozed off in the middle of questions, and abruptly awoke again, as if wondering what this was all about. But after ten minutes of relentless probing, I was able to put some kind of a report together.

The day before, David had purchased a toy called Slinky, a large but simple spring, which consisted of almost fifty feet of coiled steel wire. The spring did tricks. You set it on a stair, gave it a push, and it stepped its way down, coil after coil, like a huge, performing worm. You placed it on a chair, gave it a push and it slithered off with the same graceful uncoiling motion.

But the boys, bored at last with their TV show that night, had found still another use for the toy. Leaning out from their third-story window, they found they could extend it until one end reached the sidewalk, then with a tug bring it bounding back up again.

After a little practice, they perfected their technique to the point where passers-by on the street below were suddenly finding their hats knocked askew by a mysterious object which had disappeared by the time they looked up.

Secrecy, however, was difficult to maintain. Eventually, one of the victims, turning around for another look, spotted David leaning out the window and dropping the spring on still another pedestrian's head. Evidently a practical joker himself, he stayed to watch. Others, following his joyous stare, stopped also. In a few minutes a lot more than a handful of people had congregated, delighted by this unexpected diversion from the staid, orderly way of life on Central Park South. Two or three boys, about the age of my sons, shouted encouragement and suggested appropriate, and unsuspecting targets.

Surprised and cheered by the audience reaction, my two hopefuls redoubled their efforts and made wider and more daring attempts. At one point, an especially accurate shot by Kip hooked one end of the wire to the gold-braid epaulet of the doorman, who had emerged carrying luggage to a cab. The sight of this dignified individual attached by wire to a third-story window, apparently for quick re-entry, was an appropriate climax to the evening's performance. The crowd clapped and cheered and laughed their appreciation.

The noise brought the night manager out on the run. He took one look at the crowd, the bewildered doorman, the long wire spring, and was on the elevator to the third floor in a matter of seconds. The spring disappeared in the window for the last time, and the crowd dispersed.

Back home at last from their educational trip to the East, the boys could hardly wait to tell their friends about their adventures, which, it appeared, were two in number—the fight on the train and the episode of the spring.

"Did *you* have a nice time?" our neighbors asked Ginny and me.

"Wonderful," we insisted.

"What did you do?"

"Well," we'd say, looking around to make sure the children were not within ear shot, "one night David got hold of a spring, see? . . ."

15 · It's a Mystery to Me

"How does your poor wife manage?" they ask.

At first I resented the free use of the adjective "poor" and the accusing look that went with it. The look seemed to say, "Except for you and your uncontrolled passions, you beast, that sweet thing would be decently married to some nice millionaire who'd be content with two children at the most and would see that Ginny got some fun out of life."

I don't resent this any more because now that I know my wife better I'm convinced that she wouldn't be without children no matter who her husband was, beast or no beast.

Mostly they pity her for not having time for outside activities, such as club work, civic and school activities. As a matter of fact, however, she does have such time—not as much as do some of her friends, but what she has she uses with telling effect, as I all too well know.

The year she was president of a local mother's club she became actively concerned about the safety conditions, or lack of them, around the village schools. At the instigation of herself and several other spirited citizens, a safety committee, of which she was a star member, was formed to draw up recommendations for establishing a better rapport between motorist and pedestrian. The chief of police was summoned, impressed with the seriousness of the situation, and asked to pledge immediate action.

The chief, who felt he was already doing the best possible job, was in something less than a cooperative mood when he left the meeting. The world was against him. He was unappreciated, misunderstood, and tired. Besides, his feet hurt.

It was while he was thus reflecting on the injustices to which his job exposed him that a blue Chevrolet with several years to its credit flipped past him at questionable speed.

The chief leaped for his car. The motor roared, the wheels spun, the dust flew. The great safety drive was on.

When the driver of the blue Chevrolet was curbed, he expressed amazement at being stopped. "I was only going—" he began, in the traditional avowal of innocence.

"Things are gonna be *different* from now on," the chief growled. "Some dame has the town hepped up on safety like we never *heard* the word before. What's your name?"

"Byrnes," said the driver of the blue Chevrolet. "Thomas E. Byrnes."

The chief's pencil hung poised above the ticket.

"Byrnes, did you say?" he whispered softly. *"Byrnes?* This is wonderful," he exulted, filling out the ticket. "This is *wonderful!"*

The news that the husband of the safety drive's moving
spirit had been the first casualty spread through town like
pollen at the height of the hay-fever season. All evening I
was on the phone, receiving congratulatory messages for my
wife's effective work. "That girl has real talents," they said.
"It's high time *some*body cracked down on those speeders."

But how *does* my wife manage? I must admit it's a good
question. An average day goes something like this:

Like all families we wake up in the morning. This event
may occur any time between 5 and 7 A.M. depending on how
well rested the younger ones consider themselves to be. Between Tony, Tommy and Mary Jo there is constant rivalry
for the honor of being first into Daddy's and Mummy's room
each morning.

Often the race ends in a draw. At such times, depending
on the mood of the suddenly awakened parents, the effect
may be that of Grant's arrival at Richmond, or the sudden
bursting of the sun after a week of rain. With a shriek and
a leap they land foursquare on the bed. "Hi-yee!" they cry.
"It's morning!" They weigh us down, smother us in wild,
haymaker kisses that land with the delicacy of a wet mop,
and by constant wriggling, let us know that it's silly to think
of sleep any longer.

"Well," Ginny will say, as she has said nearly every morning of our married life, "I suppose I'd better get up." This is
a signal that it's time for *me* to get up. I am usually the first
out of bed in the morning for a reason I used to be very
reticent about until I learned over the years how many husbands get up first for the same reason: to cook breakfast, and
to cook it because they *enjoy* cooking it.

This is a custom I inherited as part of the happy kitchen

memories of my own childhood. My father would get up early each morning, shave and dress himself while the rest of the household slept, and then tiptoe to the kitchen and put the kettle on. Next, he would kneel down on the seat of a kitchen chair, and with one eye on the kettle and the other on Heaven, say his morning prayers until the kettle boiled. Then he would pour a small measure of Bushmill's Irish Whiskey into a glass, add hot water, a little sugar, a clove or two, and have his morning toddy. In later years I tried once or twice to emulate this custom, but the effect was so soothing it made me want to go back to bed. It made my father more energetic than ever.

Whether it was the sound of my father's prayers, uttered aloud in a stately, almost ominous monotone, or the fragrant odor of the hot toddy that awakened me, I don't recall but I would rush out to the kitchen in my pajamas for the great morning welcome.

Dad never disappointed me. He greeted me as if just climbing out of bed was a supreme accomplishment worthy of highest praise. Then he would perch me on the edge of the kitchen table, give me a sip of the hot toddy, and talk to me cheerfully while he cooked the breakfast.

There were few things to compare to that warm, intimate companionship, that intense feeling of father-and-son security, shared by just the two of us in the warm, intimate kitchen, among the sounds and odors of bacon and eggs crackling in the pan.

I used to think how happy he looked. Now I can understand why as I measure out the coffee and squeeze the oranges and listen for the first footsteps on the stairs.

"Daddy!" It's pudgy, four-year-old Tommy, red faced and radiant from his bed tumbling upstairs. Or it's Tony or Peggy, both shy smiling and waiting, or it's three-year-old Mary Jo, plump, tousle haired, and full of the straightforward confidence of the very young who have been told every day of their lives how wonderful they are.

So I cook breakfast while the younger ones mill around the kitchen and get in my way. Upstairs their brothers and sisters are dressing for school. Down the stair well drift the familiar queries and complaints: What dress shall I wear today, Mummy? I can't find the red sox. Do I have to wear that new shirt? The *other* kids wear blue jeans. Then Ginny's voice deciding, arranging, ordering.

A wraith-like daughter, in fresh white slip, uncombed, unshod, face gleaming from soap, whisks through the kitchen to the laundry room in search of a clean diaper for Gael Marie upstairs.

It's fruit juice, cereal, toast and milk for the smaller fry, fruit juice, cereal, toast, milk, bacon and eggs for the others. The same for Ginny and myself, except that we omit the cereal and substitute coffee for milk.

The older ones arrive now and help set the table, pour out the fruit juice, butter the toast, push up the chairs, get Mary Jo settled. Ginny comes down, or if we have some private problem to discuss, I bring up a tray for both of us when the kids aren't looking. With one ear cocked for signs of trouble below, we enjoy our quiet breakfast together.

Nina and Danielle, the two oldest girls, go into their morning delaying action. By stalling they hope to miss the bus so Daddy can drive them to school. "We *love* it when you drive us," Nina says sweetly.

The older boys get ready to leave. No stalling for them. Recently they have made the breath-taking discovery that certain children on the school bus are girls.

They come as far as the doorway to say good-by, hesitating a little longer each day over the question of whether embracing your parents is the manly thing to do. But Ginny holds out her hands to them, and they tumble into the room for the good-by kiss.

A little later, Nina appears. "Gosh, Daddy," she says, "we've *missed* the bus."

I hurriedly finish dressing, mumbling something about girls taking so long to get ready, and on my way to the office, drop them off at school.

"Could you come home early enough today to pick us up?" she asks as she gets out. "We *love* it when you pick us up."

I have no way of telling how Ginny manages things while I'm away. When I come home in the evening, there is always a dinner on the stove; the rooms, except where the seat cushions are strung together to make a train, seem to be clean and in perfect order—and this in spite of Ginny's insistence that "I was so busy with the children I didn't get a thing done today."

Not long ago she used to say this self-accusingly. Lately, however, she says it in a spirit of achievement as if proud that today at least she kept the housework from interfering with her enjoyment of her youngsters.

This change in attitude has been the product of many influences, including Mr. Briggs.

He arrived at the back door one hot Saturday afternoon with a lengthy, memorized recital of the merits of the Easy-Does-It Vacuum Cleaner.

"This wonderful machine," Mr. Briggs said, "will cut your housework in two."

At that particular moment the housework waiting to be cut

in two included a pile of laundry on the floor beside her, a stack of dishes in the sink, and beds to be made upstairs. "I'm sorry," said Ginny, anxious to get going on her chores, "but I already have a vacuum cleaner and I'm well satisfied with it."

"You'll notice," Mr. Briggs plodded on, wiping the perspiration from his face, "how many more attachments this machine has than the ordinary cleaner, which sells in most cases for as much as thirteen percent more."

"I'm sorry," Ginny repeated.

It was not difficult to feel sorry for Mr. Briggs. He was a kindly looking man, sixty-five or over, short, red faced, overheated and obviously very tired.

He leaned against the railing and continued, "I sold one only last week to Mrs. Fry in Meadowbrook Lane and she says now she doesn't understand how she ever got along without one."

Kip and Dave, meanwhile, had drifted in from the garage, and stood at the foot of the steps, idly examining Mr. Briggs' sample machine.

"Neat," said Kip, the mechanic.

"I notice you have children," Mr. Briggs went on. "Where there are children in the home—"

Nina and Danielle, pulling Tony and Tommy in a wagon, appeared from around a corner of the house.

"Well," said Mr. Briggs, "you *do* have children. All yours, I presume?"

"That's Nina and that's Danielle, and that's Tony and Tommy," Dave introduced them cordially.

"Very happy to meet you, children," said Mr. Briggs. "My," he addressed Ginny, "you *could* put this machine to good use. I know how children are around the house."

Peggy and Mary Jo clattered down from upstairs, and stood behind their mother.

"My goodness," said Mr. Briggs.

"The baby's crying," said Peggy. "I'll get her a bottle."

"The baby?" gasped Mr. Briggs, his eyes popping.

"We have nine," Ginny smiled.

"Nine! Well, isn't that wonderful? You know something? I have ten!"

"Ten!" exclaimed Ginny.

"All living," said Mr. Briggs. "A lot older than yours, of course, but, my, how wonderful it is to have a big family." He wiped his face again. "It's not easy. I know that. I have a pretty fair idea of what you're up against."

"Some days," said Ginny, "I don't know how I manage to get *anything* done."

This could obviously be a lead-in to a further sales talk about the machine that cuts work in two, but after a glance at his Easy-Does-It, Mr. Briggs said, "I can tell you about that. There's a secret to it. Don't *worry* about getting things done. It's not important."

"Why don't you come in?" asked Ginny.

"That's real nice of you," said Mr. Briggs, picking up his vacuum cleaner and following Ginny into the living room. The children followed Mr. Briggs.

"Would you like a coke?" asked Ginny.

"That would certainly hit the spot," sighed Mr. Briggs. "I find it isn't easy to get around as it used to be."

"That's a neat machine," Kip said again.

Mr. Briggs started to sit down in a chair but noticed in time that two dolls and a cap pistol were there ahead of him. He moved to another chair.

"*That's* what I mean," Ginny said. "I picked up those

things not more than fifteen minutes ago, and there they are
right back again."

"Of course you did," said Mr. Briggs with a smile of
sympathy. "How well I know. But it's sad we don't realize
how unimportant a neat room is until after the children have
grown up. I wish I still had dolls and cap pistols to remove
before sitting down at home."

Two of his boys were in the army. Two daughters and
another son were married. The rest were working or in high
school.

"How I miss them!" Mr. Briggs sighed, shaking his head.
"Thank you, son," he said as David handed him his drink.

"The rest of them want cokes now too," said David.

"Tell them to be sure to put the empty bottles where they
belong," Ginny called after him. "And turn off the stove. I
smell something burning."

"You have your hands full all right," said Mr. Briggs.
"But, Mrs. Byrnes, you must remember one thing. You'll
never lick it, no matter how hard you try. The only way to
win is to get rid of the children."

"Good heavens!" said Ginny.

"I mean it. Why, when my boy Jeff came home on furlough
last month, do you know what he wanted to do? Just sit in
the living room. Just *sit* there. Know why? Because it had
been one of the happiest rooms of his life. My wife learned
her lesson in time, God bless her. A lot of her neighbors
used to be proud of their spotless living rooms, and ours
was always messed up. My wife felt bad about that. But do
you know—a lot of those neighbors wouldn't *let* their children play in the living room. Can you imagine? Not playing
in the living room?"

He smiled this last question at the children ringed around

the room on chairs, couch and hassocks. The children looked at each other and giggled. Not play in the living room? Kip was sprawled in his favorite chair, one leg hooked over the arm. "Gosh," he said.

"I can see you've learned *your* lesson, too, Mrs. Byrnes. These kids feel at *home* here."

An hour later Mr. Briggs rose to go. "The main thing," he said, "is not to worry. They grow up so soon."

He led the way out through the dining room, through the kitchen to the back door. He led the way, Ginny knew, because he didn't want the others to see he was crying.

Once, in the kitchen, he turned enough to say, "If you're satisfied with your old machine, keep it." Out on the steps he paused once more to say good-by to the children. He patted each of the younger ones on the head. "Imagine that boy of mine," he said to Ginny, "just *sitting* there."

When he was gone, Ginny put her arms around Kip and kissed him hard on the cheek.

"That sure was a neat machine," said Kip.

But how *does* my wife get through a day? It's *still* a good question.

My present work of writing scenarios for a film producer is such—and the boss is such—that unless there are office details to attend to, I can often do my scripting at home. On these days I disappear into my "den"—a converted bedroom off the kitchen, and try to shut myself off from the rest of the house. But by the sounds drifting through the door and walls, I am able to keep pretty close tabs on what's going on.

From faraway upstairs I hear the noise of the vacuum

cleaner, the new one which Ginny later bought from Mr. Briggs, busy cutting her work in two.

Suddenly Tony and Tommy demand to be dressed for out-of-doors. The hum of the vacuum cleaner stops.

"I can't find my snow suit," says Tommy.

More silence, then the bang of the kitchen door and the kids are outside.

The sound of the washing machine and dryer take over. The kitchen door bangs again. Tony is crying that Tommy tried to bite his arm.

"Through your snow suit?" Ginny asks.

"He hit me," Tony amends the charge.

A low murmur of voices and again the kitchen door opens and bangs shut.

Around ten o'clock I convince myself I'm working too hard and step into the kitchen for a cup of coffee.

The kitchen is deserted, so I look for Ginny. She is reading the morning paper!

"How's the script coming?" she asks.

"Inspired as usual," I tell her.

"Darling, you're wonderful."

"Have a cup of coffee?" I ask.

"I'd love to," she says.

We make coffee and spend half an hour drinking it.

"You'd better get going again," Ginny says finally. I go back to my room.

Sounds now of lunch being prepared, the younger ones being called in and cleaned up for the table. Ginny's footsteps in the kitchen . . . footsteps in the breakfast nook. Telephone ringing. "Hello—oh, hello, Doris. Well, you heard about it, too?" Hours later, it seems, the receiver goes down, the door opens and closes; Ginny is out in the garden sizing up the work I will do Saturday. She says, "Hi," through the window of my room, "wish you could come out."

After lunch Tony, Tommy and Mary Jo troop up the lane to the mailbox beside the main road. Unless they know that I'm expecting an important letter, this journey can reach the proportions of a holiday excursion, with frequent stops along the way to climb the pear trees or fill their pockets with gravel from the driveway. Their purpose, of course, is to put off their afternoon nap as long as possible.

But when they know Daddy is waiting for special mail, such as a letter from his literary agent or publisher, they skip and run at full speed, top-heavy with importance. New York postmarks, which Tony has learned to identify, usually indicate a message of consequence. The red-white-and-blue border of the air-mail envelope means this is *it*—shoot the works!

"It's here!" they scream, broadcasting the news to half the neighborhood. "It's here!" Running, shouting, waving the envelope over their heads, dropping it, chasing it down wind across the field, wrestling for it, snatching it from one another, they pursue their violent and erratic way back to the house.

Exhausted, triumphant, perspiring, accusing each other of unfair practices, they rush the letter into my hands, and then, milking their roles like inveterate hams, they fall in a panting, eye-rolling heap on the floor.

At times, however, their performance ends in a nerve-shattering farce, as when the "important letter," misread by an over-anxious Tony, turns out to be a local merchant's invitation to "Act now! Don't let this great savings pass you by!"

So conscious am I of what I suppose to be the titillating effect of these demonstrations on the neighbors that at times I see in even an innocent "How are things?" a feverish curiosity to find out what the big news was *this* time.

Today, however, they return as calm as when they left. "Any mail?" I ask Tony.

"Nothing important," he says, handing me a batch of month-end bills.

They're off to take their nap at last, the baby needs feeding; the door opens again; the older ones are back from school. Cries, shouts, hurrahs! The telephone rings; I answer it. "Can Danielle stay at my house overnight?" How should *I* know? Where's Ginny? Nina, Ask your mummy to take this call, will you, dear?

Odors from the kitchen. A leg of lamb is sizzling in the oven. How did it get there? Who put those potatoes on?

Around four-thirty, Tony hesitantly pushes my door open. He knows this is against the rules, but he has suddenly remembered something vitally important.

"Daddy?"

"Well?"

"Mummy said it's your birthday next week." (It's always *some*body's birthday next week.)

"That's right."

"Well—I was wondering—what are you going to give *me?*"

This kind of question is perfectly normal for our household. It springs from a custom which, like so many in our family, took root and blossomed without encouragement from Ginny or myself.

When David, as a baby, first realized that his older brother's birthday was an occasion for celebration and gift giving, he set up a howl for special attention, too.

"He has to learn," I pontificated, "that on other people's birthdays you *give* things, not get them."

"If you can explain that to a two year old, more power to you, dear," said Ginny.

So I explained it.

"Remember, dear," I said to David, "all those nice toys you got on *your* birthday?"

"I want something *now*," David insisted.

"Of course you do," I said patiently. "But so does Kip. And it's Kip's birthday, see?"

"Why can't it be *my* birthday?"

"It *was* your birthday, remember?"

"I want my birthday *now*."

"Think, dear, what a nice big boy you'd be to *give* Kip something. Then you'd be like Mummy and Daddy."

"He wants a fire engine," said David.

This was progress. "That's the big boy," I said, patting his head.

"So do I," he added.

"Suppose you *do* get two," Ginny interposed. "Just little ones—something they can pull."

"I want a big one," said David, "with a bell."

I bought one fire engine and gave it to David to give to Kip. Surprisingly, he offered it to his brother without objection.

"Here, Kip," he said, as we had rehearsed him. "Happy birthday."

"Thanks," said Kip. "Where's yours?"

"Oh," said David, *"that's* mine. I'm only letting you play with it."

"Now just a minute," I objected.

"Wait, dear," Ginny whispered. "Let's see what happens."

"It's mine," said Kip. "You gave it to me."

"It's mine," said David. "I want it back now."

"It's mine!"

"It's mine!"

I went out to the store and bought another fire engine, which Kip presented to Dave.

"Happy birthday," said Kip.

Instead of dying out, this custom of making each birthday the common property of the others has become more firmly established, as more and more young ones have arrived to keep the tradition alive. Only after they spend a year or two in school, and learn from the other children that a birthday usually belongs to one person at a time do the older ones gradually relinquish their claim to a part in the birthday free-for-alls.

So now I tell Tony I haven't decided yet what to give him on my birthday, and he tells me he's going to give me a new lawn mower.

"But for me," he sighs, as he reaches the door, "I think a little fire engine would be nice."

"Okay—a fire engine."

"And one for Tommy too."

Dinner. Television. Dolly-buggy repairs. Homework. "Can't I stay up a *little* longer?"

The smaller ones have to go to bed. Thank Heaven, their

pajamas are so handy. "Daddy, will you tell us a story?" Don't their beds look fresh and inviting?

Guess I'll have a last smoke. See my pipe around anywhere, dear? Thanks.

It's been a long day. I pick up my pajamas, bathrobe, and slippers, not where I left them this morning, but right where they're supposed to be; I pull back the covers of the perfectly made bed and turn in. By the way, dear, did you remember to call the plumber about that leaky bathroom faucet? You did? And the fellow about the storm windows? Fine.

Nowadays when people get that accusing look in their eye, I beat them to the punch. "Greatest mystery to me," I say, before they can open their mouths, "is how my wife does it."

16 · Just Like His Father

One of the most selfish and persistent hopes of fatherhood
is that one or more offspring will show talents that unmis-
takably come straight from the old man.

Since writing, in one form or another, has always been my
livelihood, I assumed that as soon as Kip and David had
mastered the alphabet, they would begin composing stories.
Instead, they continued their favorite occupation of drawing
horses.

To help nourish the writing talent I knew must be there,
I diligently read them all the classic bedtime stories, Mother-
Goose rhymes, and fairy tales I could get my hands on. The
boys were patient but not impressed.

Then one night, having temporarily exhausted our bedtime library, I made the mistake of offering to spin them a story out of my head. They agreed it was worth a try.

I hadn't gone very far before I realized that a little more preparation would have been a good thing, but I doggedly plowed ahead.

The stories, which became the prototype for dozens of others, concerned the adventures of a child prodigy named Johnny Poopadook. Johnny's great talent, as it developed, was for saving his slow-witted father from a variety of violent deaths.

In the initial story, for instance, Johnny, by means of a helicopter and long rope that happened to be handy (the boys grew to love the word "happened"), lifted his old man out of an abandoned well into which he had fallen on his way home from work one night. The presence of an escaped circus lion gave the plot extra zest.

The reaction to this first of the Poopadook stories surpassed all expectations. They squealed, bounced up and down on the bed, begged for more, and refused to go to sleep until I promised a similar story for the next night.

My delight at their reaction was somewhat tempered by the thought that if this is the kind of stuff they like, their tastes can't be very good. I tried once or twice to improve the tone of the stories, but I was swiftly and loudly put straight. Once or twice, also, I started to switch to something else, like *Treasure Island,* that had made my blood run cold on more than one occasion when I was a boy. My offspring couldn't understand why so much time was wasted with description, and clamored again for more of J.P., as I had nicknamed him for the sake of brevity.

I checked with Ginny and was told there was no use blaming this on her side of the family. She and her brother had both read Shakespeare by the time they were ten. Her younger sisters were standouts in school. It was simply a case of blood not "telling."

Well, I thought, perhaps they *are* too young to display any taste for literature. Maybe a few years of schooling will do the trick.

When Kip was in fourth grade, Ginny and I visited his teacher, a twinkly-eyed, but slightly puzzled nun, to get the first of several "reports to parents" on our son's progress for the year to date.

"You know, Mr. Byrnes," she began ominously, "I don't want you to think Kippy is a difficult child or backward. But he does present me with certain problems."

Her hands were absently fingering the beads of the enormous rosary that hung from her waist, as if she were offering up silent prayers for the student in question.

"You see," she said, "I have always tried to give the children every possible opportunity to use their imagination, to invent things. Several times a week we have a story hour, in which the children take turns telling the class some little yarn they've made up."

Ah, I thought, and our family representative stands before them all tongue-tied and mute.

"The first day we did this, everything went along just fine. The children were understandably shy at first, but in time this wore off. Your son, however, was the exception."

"He was?"

"He seemed quite the opposite of shy. In fact he was fairly bursting with eagerness."

"This is Kip you're talking about?" I asked, in astonishment.

"Your son," she assured me. "Of course, that part of it—

the eagerness to tell a story, I mean—was wonderful. I was delighted. *Until* I heard the story. Mr. Byrnes," she said, looking me straight in the eye, "wherever did he pick up those outrageous stories about a nasty little character named Johnny Poopadook?"

I could only shake my head numbly.

"Why," she said, "they're downright sadistic! The things that happen to the father! And Johnny, the things *he* does for a child."

"I suppose," I mumbled, red faced, "the class was scandalized."

"Scandalized nothing," she said with spirit. "That's the part I *don't* like—they *love* those stories. Why wouldn't they love them? They appeal to their baser natures. A child perpetually proving himself smarter than his father. Was there ever anything so ridiculous?"

She was getting a little too close to home on that last one.

"Every time I announce a story hour now, the class calls for Kippy to tell another tale about this Poopadook character. Why, children in *second* grade should have more intelligence than to listen to such stories!"

"All right," I promised. "You'll hear no more stories about Johnny Poopadook. I'll see to that."

"I wouldn't just shut Kip up, Mr. Byrnes," she advised me. "I'd try to put something better into his head. Why don't you leave some good children's books lying around so he can pick them up occasionally?"

Oh, Lord, I thought, how many times have I left good books lying around, only to be tripped over or pushed aside. But I'll try again.

I tried with everything I knew. I tried *Treasure Island* again. I tried the best of the *Leatherstocking Tales*. I even tried him with my old hero, Zane Grey; I tried him with Tom Swift and the Rover Boys and Tom Playfair, and Dick Prescott, and the Motorcycle Boys in Yellowstone Park. It was no use.

"Too much description," said Kip.

At times I was sure I could see indications of better things to come. "You and Mummy be the audience," Kip said one evening when he was eleven. "We're going to put on a play in the dining room. You sit in the living room next to the piano."

"A play!" I said. "That's wonderful. Who wrote it?"

"It isn't written," he explained. "We kind of make it up as we go along."

"Have you rehearsed it?" I asked.

"Nope—but we talked about it. Don't worry," he reassured me, with the confidence of an old pro, "it'll work out all right. I'll help the girls along if they get stuck."

The dining-room table and chairs had been pushed to one side, Kip supervising, Dave doing most of the pushing. Ginny and I were made to take our seats, and were told not to ask questions about the noises in the kitchen, which led off the dining room. The kitchen, it seemed, was the dressing room, and the cast, which included, besides Kip and Dave, Nina, Danny, Peggy and Tony, was busy making up. They were also deciding who was to play what role.

The play was to be the adventures of Christopher Columbus, considerably streamlined, and Kip, in addition to being director, producer, stage manager and prompter, was the star.

"You'll be Columbus' mother, Danielle," said Nina. "I'll be Queen Isabella of Spain."

"Why can't *I* be Queen Isabella?"

"Danielle will be the cook on the boat," Kip settled the argument. "Besides," he added authoritatively, "who ever heard of Columbus' mother?"

Peggy, then three, was to be Columbus' son, a part she objected to violently because it didn't give her a chance to wear a certain old hat of her mother's. Dave was to play a shipbuilder in act one, and the first mate of the *Santa Maria* in act two. Nina, as the Spanish queen, was dressed in an old skirt, blouse and scarf of Ginny's, and waved a battered umbrella as her queenly sceptre.

When everyone was ready, Kip shooshed them to be quiet and stepped to the center of the dining-room floor to deliver a prologue.

"This is the story of Christopher Columbus," he announced. "The first thing you're going to see is Columbus buying a boat."

He bowed stiffly and made his exit walking backwards. Immediately Dave emerged almost lost in a pair of my pants, my hat down over his ears, a hammer in one hand and a fistful of nails in the other.

"Don't worry," he stopped to assure his startled audience, "I'm not *really* going to hit the nails; I'll just pretend."

He pulled a chair to the middle of the stage, and proceeded to hammer imaginary boards in place all around it.

After a few seconds of this, he grew impatient and motioned Kip to come on.

"It's too soon," Kip whispered from the doorway.

"I could have built *two* ships," Dave grumbled.

Kip finally clomped onto the stage, swaggering like a cowboy.

"Hiya," he greeted the shipbuilder.

"Hi," answered David.

"How's the ship coming?" he asked, giving a fair, though unintentional, imitation of Gary Cooper at his wild-western best.

"Not bad," said the shipbuilder conservatively.

"Sure she doesn't leak?" asked Columbus. "I gotta have a ship that doesn't leak."

"When do *I* come in?" Nina asked from the wings.

"Don't forget," said Danielle, "I'm the cook."

"Be quiet," growled Kip.

"My ships never leak," said the shipbuilder. Then he went into one of his familiar giggling fits. He knew what Kip was going to say next; it was the punch line from which the whole idea of the play had sprung.

"I dunno," said Kip, giggling himself. "I hear they call you Leaky Joe."

The show stopped in its tracks while the entire cast roared its appreciation.

"Okay," said Kip finally, trying to restore order. "See that it's finished on time."

"Where you goin' in 'er?" asked the shipbuilder.

Another punch line. "America! Where do you *think* Columbus went?" The girls in the kitchen clapped.

Kip walked off, then immediately returned, furious at himself. "Aw, gosh," he said, "we got mixed up. We should have started with the court of Isabella."

"That's easy," said David, still hammering nails, "let's just forget the last scene."

The court of Queen Isabella was quickly staged by moving an armchair to the center of the floor. Nina then entered, holding the umbrella like a flaming sword, informed us that she was Queen Isabella and sat down.

"Come on in," she invited Columbus.

Columbus, still playing Gary Cooper, slouched up to the queen and gave her his standard greeting. "Hiya," he said. Peggy plodded in after him, sliding along in my bedroom slippers. "You didn't wait for me," she accused Columbus.

Nina meanwhile was fluffing up the old dress and straightening the hat. She smiled at her mother. "Isn't it nice?" she asked.

"You're supposed to ask what I'm here for," said Kip sternly.

"What are you here for?" asked the obliging queen.

"I want to discover America, but I'll need a boat."

"Very good, Columbus," said the queen. "I'll give you a boat."

"All I need is the money. I'll buy it myself."

"Very good," said the queen. She dug into the folds of the dress and then slapped imaginary coin into Columbus' outstretched hand.

"Thanks," said Columbus. "That's the end of *that* scene," he informed his audience.

They skipped the shipyard scene, because, after all, we'd had it. Our next view of Columbus was on board the *Santa Maria*, where he paced the deck with great vigor. David, standing on a chair, was on the lookout for land. Another chair Danielle was using as a stove. This silent tableau went on for nearly a minute when Danielle urged somebody to say something.

"It's awful dark up here," David supplied.

"Tell me, O Lookout," said Columbus in his first approach to dramatic speech, "do you see any land?"

The lookout peered intently along the north wall of the dining room. "Very little," he said.

"Darn it," said Columbus, and resumed his pacing. "Columbus was worried," he informed Ginny and me, in case we were wondering why all the pacing. "It says so in our history book."

"He sure was," I encouraged him.

"You're all doing fine," said Ginny.

"*Now* do you see any land?" Columbus asked, in a voice that meant either you see land, Brother, or turn in your grease paint.

"Yep," said the lookout, who was becoming a little bored himself, "*now* I see it."

"Good," said Columbus. He was about to announce the end of the play, but Danielle, the cook, who hadn't enjoyed a line so far, was way ahead of him.

"Time for dinner!" she called. "Everybody down for dinner. Bacon and eggs," she added.

The discovery of America was forgotten for the moment while the crew assembled for their evening meal. The play, which so far in less than five minutes had covered a shipyard, the court of a queen, and the deckboard scene at the sighting of land, now slowed down to a ten-minute enactment of chowtime aboard the *Santa Maria*. Danielle was in her element serving imaginary bacon and eggs, pouring coffee, making toast and squeezing oranges.

If she thought the action dragged, she chirped, "Have some more," and went through the whole cooking routine again.

Peggy, Columbus' son, became so bored with it all that she finally walked off stage.

"Yipe!" yelled Danielle, "Peggy's walking on the water!"

Nina complained from the doorway that Danielle was just prolonging the meal so she'd have all those lines.

"I guess we've had enough to eat," Columbus at last told the cook. He walked to the center of the stage. "Well," he said, "I guess that's the end of the play."

Ginny and I clapped loud and long.

"We *loved* it," Ginny assured them.

The cast, unequal to the applause, milled about the stage aimlessly. Then the boys, to cover their embarrassment, began to wrestle. The girls exchanged costumes and turned the rest of the evening into a style show.

"Now, Tim, honestly," said Ginny later, "don't you think it was something even to *want* to put on a play?"

"I honestly do," I said. I felt reassured. "We must stimulate them all we can."

"Oh, yes, we *must.*"

A few days later, however, at Ginny's suggestion that they try another play, the boys demurred.

"That's kid stuff," said David.

"Corny," said Kip.

The few plays that were subsequently produced got along with an all-girl cast.

The more I think about it, the more I realize that children are just as much individuals as their parents. Was I a writer because my father had been a writer? My father had been a salesman. So why should my children be writers? A writer's life, in spite of a lot of nonsense that has been written about it, is not easy. All too often the rewards are small. Probably no vocation is attended with so much worry, so much dependence on other people's tastes, so much disappointment —disappointment when your work is not accepted; disappointment when it is, because it seldom reads the way you thought it should.

No, that's not the life to wish on my children. I should be glad, I tell myself, that they show no interest at all in writing. I should thank God He made them what they are—tuba players and who knows what else?

Then one evening Nina comes down from her room, stands before my chair, and says timidly, "Daddy—would you like me to read you a story I wrote?"

"My *darling!*" I answer.

17 · Uncles and Aunts

One of the best things about having a lot of children is that you provide *their* children with a lot of uncles and aunts. And next to having parents, nothing is quite so important to the development of a full and satisfying childhood as having a father or mother with plenty of brothers and sisters.

With unclehood and aunthood go certain prerogatives and pleasures that even the great estate of parenthood cannot claim. Uncles and aunts are always favorite people when you're a child because they give you all the candy and cake you can hold at one sitting; and by the time the resultant tummyache sets in, you've gone home, or they've gone home, and it's your parents you associate with the cramps and sudden trips to the bathroom.

Uncles and aunts are always glad to see you. You never bore them. Because if you start to bore them, they leave. Only your parents must hang around right up to bedtime, answering endless questions about why are you my daddy, and does God know it when we brush our teeth without using the toothpaste? And why, why, why?

With the exception of Ginny's married sister, Stephanie, and my uncle, Monsignor Daniel Byrnes, our relatives are now scattered pretty widely over the U.S. and see us only on very rare occasions. But Aunt Stephanie and her husband, Dick, live only ten miles south of us in another village, and though a trip to her house takes only a few minutes, the children regard it with all the excitement of a trip to the moon. Especially Tony, a great "family man."

For days in advance of his first visit, his bag—an old briefcase of mine—was packed and ready. A dozen times during his waking hours, he would pick up some treasured toy and add it to the bundle. "I'll need this," he'd say, as if preparing to be gone for months.

When Stephanie called to pick him up, he was in top spirits, kissing his sisters fond good-by and assuring Tommy, his buddy, that he'd call him on the phone every day. He told his mother not to worry, and promised me he'd be a good boy and remember to say his grace-before-meals without fail.

Our phone rang early the next morning.

"I'm ready to come home now," said the voice of Tony.

"But, darling," said Ginny, "you just got there."

"I know, but I'm ready to come home now."

"But Stephanie can't be running out here so often, dear. She has her own babies to look after."

"I know," said Tony, "but I'm ready to come home now."

When Stephanie's husband arrived home from work that evening, Tony was more than ever ready to come home now; in fact with tears and lamentations he *insisted* on coming home now.

There was nothing for Stephanie and Dick to do but bundle up their own children—a pair of month-old twins—pack Tony's belongings, delay their dinner, and return their nephew to the bosom of his family.

Tony arrived as gay and debonair as a seasoned traveler returning from a summer on the Continent. He embraced Tommy, kissed his mother and me, and gave us great, rambling accounts of what he said to the butcher and what the butcher said to him, and how the policeman winked at him and he winked back.

Tommy was goggle-eyed. "A real policeman?"

"A real policeman," Tony said lightly.

Stephanie was broken hearted. She was sure she had failed in her first real test as an aunt.

But she needn't have worried. As they drove away, no one was more demonstrative in waving good-by or sorrier to see her go than Tony.

"Gosh, Mummy," he said, "was it ever fun! Can I go back tomorrow?"

Next to Christmas and Easter, the highspots of the children's year were the almost monthly visits of their Great Uncle Dan, my father's brother, whose monsignor's purple didn't stop him from being as playful and gay as his seventy-odd years would allow.

His happy informality was all the more welcome to me personally because it stood in such marked contrast, through no fault of his, to my own youthful experiences with him.

A tall, broad-shouldered man of notable dignity, he had become in my early years a rather formidable figure because my parents were always holding him up to me as the model for all the gentlemanly virtues they hoped I would eventually possess. Did I come to the table with hands unwashed, or say, "Shut up" to the little girl next door? The unfailing corrective was the solemn question, "Would Uncle Dan ever do a thing like that?"

My boyhood visits to his parish house were strictly formal; I had been coached to be nothing else, because my father and mother wanted Uncle Dan to know what a well-mannered offspring they were raising. Before setting out, I would be admonished not to sniffle or rub my nose with my bare hand, and if I had to use the bathroom, I was to say, "Excuse me, please, Uncle Dan," and not "I gotta go to the bathroom." Most important of all, I was to be sure, at all times, to ask specifically how he was feeling.

Once after an afternoon visit that was merry in spite of these encumbrances, I was half a block from his house on the way home when I realized I had forgotten to ask after his health, which was obviously excellent. But how could I tell my parents he merely *looked* good to *me?* So I promptly returned to his door and rang his bell.

His housekeeper informed me he had gone over to the parish school next door to see the janitor about something.

I found him at last in the boiler room inspecting the coal supply.

"Well, Junior," he said. "I thought you'd gone."

"I forgot something important," I said. "How are you?"

He understood perfectly. "Tell them I'm fine, Junior," he replied.

Now, with my own father dead, and Uncle Dan the only one left of that family that had also once numbered nine children, he became a second father to me, and the greatest of great uncles to our youngsters.

Rarely did he visit us empty handed. On certain Sunday afternoons the car would roll up the driveway, his assistant, Father Stephen O'Donnell, at the wheel, and himself half buried beneath a tumble of packages. He was the uncle who got us our first horse. He brought a huge plastic wading pool, a bicycle for Danielle, a play-yard slide, and baskets of fruit and gifts for Ginny and myself. He was inordinately proud of his great-nephews and nieces, and was greatly impressed by the fact that the present generation of Byrneses now numbered the same as did the family of his own father and mother.

One day, he brought the greatest surprise of all—the Bishop of Kilimanjaro, Tanganyika, Africa.

The bishop, an old friend of his from other years, missed being a Byrnes by one "s," an omission which diminished his enjoyment of life not a whit. He had come to America for a brief stay, and was delighted by the monsignor's invitation to spend a day in the country with our family.

The *size* of the family, however, as I learned later, did not become a topic of conversation until the trip from Uncle Dan's parish in Chicago was well under way.

"And how many children does Thomas have?" asked the bishop.

"Ah," sighed the monsignor, " 'tis the sorrow of my life. He has only one."

"D'you tell me now?" said the bishop. "And how long has he been married?"

"Sixteen years. Long enough to have had more than one."

"Long enough indeed," murmured the bishop.

"It's a sad state of affairs," said Father O'Donnell, doing the driving as usual, and cueing in like an old trouper.

"Is it the wife, d'you think?" asked the bishop, squinting an inquisitive eye at my uncle.

"She's the salt of the earth. She'd have a dozen if he'd let her."

"Ah," said the bishop sadly. "So often it's the husband. Afraid of the responsibility, I suppose?"

The monsignor nodded his head. Father O'Donnell nodded *his* head. The thing was too big for words.

"You don't suppose," said the bishop, searching in his kindly way for an excuse, "there's any physical reason?"

"Poof!" exclaimed the monsignor.

"They're both as healthy as trouts," said Father O'Donnell.

"It's the responsibility then."

"It might very well be," said the monsignor.

"I'll have a quiet talk with Thomas in the garden," said the bishop. "He has a garden, has he?"

"He has," said the monsignor. "Big enough for all the children in *Tipperary*."

"You poor man," soothed the bishop. "But don't worry. I'll have a talk with him."

The bishop was a lively, humorous man with sparkling eyes set in a face that was strong, but as gently moulded as a young boy's. His look, however, when I first greeted him, was one of frosty disapproval. The monsignor and Father O'Donnell, meanwhile, had become absorbed in admiration of the distant landscape.

The children, for the moment, were still upstairs, where Ginny was giving them their final inspection. Tony, at the

last minute, had gone wading in the fish pond with his shoes
on and had to be changed. Mary Jo had taken her hair ribbon
off and tied it to the collie. Kip and Dave were putting up
their final resistance to a change of shirts.

I led the bishop around the side of the house to the porch.
The monsignor and Father O'Donnell trailed behind, still
fascinated by the far-away arrangement of tree tops, sky and
clouds.

The bishop remarked stiffly, "You have a beautiful place
here, my son. 'Tis a blessing to have all this room."

"It certainly is," I agreed. "A great place for children."

The bishop threw me a look as cold as a December morning. Was I laughing in the face of God?

I offered him a highball, a glass of beer, a cup of tea—
anything—but he quietly refused. Could I take his coat?
Out here in the country, I assured him, we're pretty informal.
No thank you. He was quite comfortable.

"The others will be down in a few minutes," I said.

Uncle Dan and Father O'Donnell were making a great
show of inspecting one of the porch screens, which Tommy
had perforated with a pencil.

Finally there was the clump-clump of a pair of number
twelves on the inside stairs, and Kip slouched onto the porch,
still unhappy about the change of shirts.

"This is Kip, Your Grace," I introduced him. "Bishop
Byrne, Kip, all the way from Africa."

The bishop held out his ring to be kissed, in keeping with
the ancient custom.

"A fine strapping boy," he said over his outstretched arm.
"A few more of these wouldn't hurt anyone now, would
they?"

Kip stepped back to let me introduce David.

"This is my second oldest, Your Grace."

"Second?" the bishop asked uncertainly. "I understood your uncle to say—"

"They could do with a little more industry around here," the monsignor was telling Father O'Donnell as he poked his finger through the holes in the screening.

"A bit of wire and you'd think a fellow could fix a little thing like this in two minutes," said Father O'Donnell.

"This is Nina and Danielle," I said to the bishop.

"Nina *who?*" he asked.

"They're both mine," I answered, perplexed.

A second later Ginny appeared with Peggy, Tony, Tommy and Mary Jo trotting beside her, as fresh and fluffy as young goslings. Gael Marie was in her arms.

"And these?" stuttered the bishop, his face getting red.

"You've met them all," I said. "Four boys and five girls. And this is my wife."

The bishop faced Father O'Donnell and Uncle Dan with the slow, ominous movement of a man carefully dredging the nethermost reaches of his vocabulary for its most thunderous malediction.

Then suddenly his sense of humor ignited and he seemed to explode in a great gust of laughter. The monsignor and Father O'Donnell bent double. The rest of us stood in open-mouthed astonishment.

"Ho-ho-ha-hee!" the bishop gasped. "Afraid of the responsibility! Ho-ho-hee-ha!"

"The sorrow of the monsignor's life!" panted Father O'Donnell.

"You must have a talk with him in the garden!" the monsignor roared.

"By jingo," exclaimed the bishop, "this is going to be fun!"

Here," he said, handing Kip his coat, "hang that up like a good lad and tell your father I'll have a drop of Scotch with a little plain water."

Within an hour the bishop was exhausted. Kip and Dave insisted on marching him out behind the woods for target practice with their twenty-two rifle. He had to inspect the horses, and only by my firm insistence that the boys behave themselves was he saved from having to prove he could ride bareback.

The older girls showed him the fruits of their year's dancing lessons, and nothing would do but that he line up with them and see if he could kick his heels as high as theirs.

The younger ones waited like spiders till he seated himself, and once he did, they swarmed over him unmercifully.

"Bishop," the monsignor warned him at one point, "if you're going to have that talk in the garden, you'd better get it over with. It's late."

"You can just mind your ecclesiastical business," said the bishop, making a lunge for Peggy.

It was dusk before they left. "I'll never forget this," the bishop said, as he stood beside the car. "I'll never forget it."

The children would not forget it either.

"Kneel down now," said the bishop, "and I'll give you my blessing."

We knelt in the gravel of the driveway. ". . . In nomine Patris, et Filii, et Spiritus sancti" . . .

Kip and Dave had saddled their horses. As the car turned into the lane that leads to the main road, they galloped beside it, waving like rodeo riders and shouting, "Good-by, Bishop! . . . Good-by, Father Steve! . . . Good-by, Uncle Dan!"

18 · Happy Father's Day!

From overhead as I write, come sounds of the older children getting ready for bed. The younger ones are already asleep.

Except Mary Jo. A sudden thump on the floor above, a quick determined patter of three-year-old feet in the direction of the big bedroom, bespeak her final, almost nightly, protest at being put to bed "so early." In a little while I will find her, thumb in mouth, sound asleep on the coverlet of the big bed. I will carry her back to her own room, and as I lay her down, she will open one eye and give me a look that says, "Putting *me* to bed isn't quite as easy as you think, is it?"

A few minutes ago I sat on the edge of Tony's bed and told him and Tommy and Mary Jo a good-night story, as a few short years ago I told stories to Kip and Dave.

Johnny Poopadook, however, has stepped aside for the Brave Engineer (Tony), the Fearless Fireman (Tommy), and the Patient Passenger (Mary Jo). Their imaginary locomotive is back in the garage beside the car (and the horses and dogs) after heroically rescuing a trainload of people stranded in a snowdrift on the Chicago, Milwaukee, and St. Paul.

This has been a wonderful day!

It began with a shriek. "Happy Father's Day!" Nina yelled about 6:30 A.M., as she and Danielle tumbled into our room. "Happy Father's Day!" called Peggy, "happy Father's Day!"

In a moment the bed was swarming with children. "This is your day, Daddy! Mummy told us!" I felt as if the whole world were celebrating a single-handed founding of the Republic by Byrnes.

"We have a surprise for you!" Nina exclaimed. "You stay right here in bed. Danny and I are going to make breakfast and bring it up to you on a tray!" Having breakfast on a tray, in our house, is like having breakfast on the St. Regis Roof.

The kitchen below us became alive with the clatter of pans, the banging of cabinet doors, and the rattle of silverware. "I'm making the toast! . . . No, *I'm* making the toast —you're fixing the cereal. . . . Well! And I suppose you're frying the bacon and eggs, too! . . . Of course I am; you're making the coffee! . . . I thought *you* were making the coffee and I was squeezing the oranges. . . ."

At frequent intervals, Tony, Tommy and Mary Jo would pound upstairs to report on the progress in the kitchen. "The cereal is ready! . . . They're frying the bacon and eggs now! . . . I saw the toast! . . . They have the tray almost ready!" And finally, "Here they come! Sit up, sit up!"

Orange juice ("You can have the prunes if you want"), corn flakes, bacon, eggs, toast and coffee! And in the center of the tray, in a tall waterglass, a handful of petunias from the garden.

"I'm sure hungry," said Tony.

"He hasn't eaten yet," Nina explained. "We were too busy getting *your* breakfast."

"Can I have a piece of bacon?" asked Mary Jo.

"Don't bother Daddy," said Danielle. "This is *his* breakfast and Mummy's."

"I'm hungry," said Mary Jo.

"Here, dear," said Ginny. "Here's a piece of bacon."

"No, no!" shrieked Nina. "This is your breakfast!"

"I'm hungry," said Mary Jo.

"Don't worry, darling," Ginny told Nina. "It's a wonderful breakfast."

"I like orange juice," said Tommy.

"Here," I said, "have some."

"No," said Nina, but she could see it was a losing battle. She skipped downstairs. "I'll make some more of everything," she called after her.

After breakfast Danielle announced, "And now we're going to give you your Father's Day presents."

Ginny had told me about the presents. Yesterday, with our car in a Chicago parking lot, waiting my return from a business trip, the three oldest girls had walked the two miles into the village to buy me their gifts. It had been a hot and dusty day, so hot in fact that the local garage man, seeing the girls trudging up the highway, had been moved to tell them, "When you're through shopping, come back to the garage and I'll drive you home."

From money they had been saving for more than a month they bought me a pipe, a cigarette lighter, and a tiny framed picture of Lake Louise at sunset. "We spent everything," Nina said proudly. "We didn't even have enough left to buy a coke."

David, however, was downcast. "I bought Daddy some cuff links," he grumbled, "but I hid them so the girls wouldn't find them and tell, and now I can't find them myself."

Later that morning, Danielle was putting some baby clothes into the washing machine. "Daddy!" she called. "I found the cuff links."

"That's right!" David hollered from the front room. *"Now* I remember."

Kip had been missing from the family circle since six o'clock that morning when he had dressed, gone quietly off to church and then to the local golf course to caddy, as he had been doing the last few Sundays.

By one o'clock, the regular dinner time, there was no sign of him. Two hours later, with dinner over, he had still not appeared. "This is overdoing it," I told Ginny. "He knows we want him home for dinner."

Ginny, I thought, was more patient than usual, and not the least bit worried. "It may have been a long game," she said vaguely.

"He's probably loafing around the corner drug store," I growled. I began to devise suitable forms of chastisement for such disobedience. "Wait'll I lay my hands on him!"

"Now, Timmy," was all Ginny said.

Four o'clock came and went. So did five. At six o'clock I called the golf course, but to whoever answered the phone

one caddy was pretty much like another. "How do *I* know where he is?" a weary voice answered. "Most of the kids have gone home."

"Did you hear that?" I asked Ginny. "The other kids have gone home."

"Darling," Ginny said. "Here he comes now."

I hurried outside to the foot of the backsteps to be in position for the opening shot.

Up the long driveway from the main road came a weary, gangly figure on a bicycle. His face was red with the day's heat. His hair hung like wet tassles over his forehead. His legs moved as if they could hardly give the pedals another turn.

But under his arm was a package, wrapped in white.

There have been all too many times in my life when a treacherous temper made me speak out of turn, but, miraculously, this was not one of them. I watched, silent, and waited until I could make out the expression on his face.

It was one of triumph. As he pedaled to a stop, he held out a package, that from its shape could be nothing else than a box of cigars.

"I had to work a little longer to earn all the money," he panted, and added proudly, "They're the best you can get."

Whenever I am asked, as I am asked frequently, "How can you afford so many children?" I make polite mumblings to the effect that, "Oh, we get along."

This, I know, is a very unsatisfactory answer. Many of the people who ask the question would appreciate a much more business-like reply, something you might formulate as an economic thesis labeled "Children Do Pay Off," or "It's Smart to Have a Large Family." "We'd have that many children ourselves if we could afford them," they say accusingly, even though in many cases their income is far more substantial than mine.

When it comes right down to it, I don't suppose I can afford them. Maybe they *are* a luxury. But they are a luxury for which Ginny and I have been willing to forego other, more popular luxuries when necessary, and for which I have been able to work harder than I might have worked without them (but no harder than necessary). There is no doubt about it, like so many large families, we have been very "lucky" and there have been many times when we were quite sure that certain prayers were being answered.

But the economic arguments against having children don't bother me any more. I have learned that there are so many more convincing reasons for not having them, if you are really *looking* for reasons.

In the first place, who *can* afford them, or rather, how does anyone *know* ahead of time whether he can afford them? We decide whether or not we can afford a new automobile because the salesman gives us firm figures on price and delivery. Experience gives us a fair estimate of the car's daily upkeep. Insurance protects us against most unplanned expenses like broken fenders or broken arms.

But what's the price of a baby—its operating costs? It may be the mother's life! It may be a drastic rearranging of family plans for the future. Experience is of little help. The experience of the uneventful birth of Kip in no way prepared us, a short time later, for the experience of having both Ginny quarantined with scarlet fever and Kip quarantined in my parents' house with whooping cough, while at the same time, in the hospital, his stomach closed with pyloric stenosis, two-week-old David was beginning a life-or-death fight that would last for more than a month. I doubt if I was able to afford the cold fear I felt at the sound of the doctor's voice, at one point, summoning me to the hospital in the middle of the night because the baby had "suddenly taken a turn for the worse."

The wonder of it is that so many babies are born at all! Their sales approach is salesmanship at its bungling worst.

In effect, the child-to-be says to its prospective father, "You'll have to buy me sight unseen. I have no references of any kind, no speed record to point to with pride, no reputation for economy, not even a thirty-day guarantee. My top, for instance, may not even be the color you prefer, and as for body styling, what if I should grow up to look like Uncle George?"

Here and there we may find a father who answers, "But you'll be soft and cute, and it will be a rewarding experience to watch you become more and more aware of the world around you. And I'll get a kick out of showing you off to friends."

It must be admitted, however, that the more practical father-to-be will not always consider the baby's softness or cuteness sufficient compensation for the rude 2 A.M. awakenings other parents have described to him so vividly. Nor will his pride at showing the baby off outweigh the colds and tummy aches he is sure will develop just as he is leaving for his first evening out in a long strenuous month. And on quiet Sunday afternoons, the breadwinner's classic time for napping, the baby will undoubtedly want to be read to or taken out for an airing. And the baby's mother will be all for it.

On the other hand, he must admit that some of the fathers of his acquaintance have spoken enthusiastically of the fun you have with a child around. Keeps you young, he has heard it said. He himself may not be worried as yet about growing old, but even so, it *would* be pretty stimulating to teach a son for the first time how to hold a baseball bat, bait a hook or send messages up a string to a kite.

Wouldn't it?

But what if the child is a girl? Well, he could build her a dollhouse, couldn't he? A fine big one with electric lights inside. Didn't he always get a kick out of making things?

But could he stand the emotional strain if the child became seriously ill?

Wasn't his friend Byrnes telling him just the other day about the time when young David hitched a ride on a milk truck, fell off, and lay unconscious on the street while his older brother, Kip, raced home screaming hysterically that David was dead? Is all this happy talk about babies worth an experience like that?

With no child around to help you decide, the answer is apt to be no.

But then for various reasons—perhaps because his wife wants a baby so much, or because he feels that with so many other people having babies, he would eventually feel cheated if he didn't have one—his child is born.

It may be a girl instead of the boy he wanted. Its hair, what there is of it, is not at all the red he had hoped for, and—who knows?—its body styling could very well be that of Uncle George.

But by now it doesn't matter. The sale has been made!

19 · A Wonderful House for Children

Mr. Van Ettig, the real-estate man, surprised us with a phone call the other day.

"I was just wondering," he said, "if you people might have changed your minds about staying."

Even though the changing of our minds for the past six years has become as predictable as the changing of the tides, there was no sarcasm in his voice. Mr. Van Ettig might have been asking whether the swallows were coming back this year to Capistrano. But it was not yet spring, our usual changing-of-the-mind season; in fact he telephoned three days before Christmas.

The house was alive with the holiday spirit. At the dining-room table, piled high with colored paper, foil, ribbons,

sequins, string and glue, the girls and their mother were busy
making tree ornaments and trimming wreaths. Outside the
front door David, with verbal assists from Tommy, was string-
ing colored lights. In the basement Kip was painting the trim
on a special present we were making for Tony, the "brave
engineer,"—a locomotive big enough to accommodate him inside its cab, with foot pedals he could pump to make it go.
Outside, Tony himself, suspicious of the secret basement
activities from which he and the younger ones had been
barred for a week, circled the house in hopes of finding a
window that would afford him a peek into the workshop.
Each time his figure shadowed the glass, Kip would shout:
"Get away from there, Tony—you're stepping on the flowers!"

"What flowers?" Tony would ask. "It's all *snow* out here."

"The flowers *under* the snow," Kip would retort, and
Tony, for the time being, would retreat.

"If you are thinking of selling," Mr. Van Ettig was saying
as though the "if" were entirely superfluous, "I have someone
who might be interested."

"Aren't you rushing it a bit?" I asked.

Mr. Van Ettig laughed. "It *is* out of season, I'll admit, but
there's a man here in my office who has just been transferred
from the East and he's desperate to find a place in a hurry.
I thought your house would be perfect. He has six children.
. . . Excuse me a moment."

There were sounds of a hurried conference at the other
end of the line.

"Mr. Wells tells me there's a seventh on the way," Mr.
Van Ettig amended. "Due in two months."

This bit of biological information about the Wells family
may sound entirely superfluous to the uninitiated, but I had

used the same technique myself on occasion. Mr. Wells intended to conjure up irresistible pictures of six shelterless
children, a wife in labor, a harassed father trying bravely
to keep them warm and dry as they squatted on a curbstone
somewhere in the worst blizzard of the decade.

"Well," I said sympathetically, "to tell the truth we
aren't—"

"Mr. Wells has seen the picture I took of your place,"
Mr. Van Ettig interrupted. "He says it's *exactly* what he's
looking for."

I had the uncomfortable feeling that the Wells family was
already moving in the front door and we were being pushed
out the back.

"Mr. Wells," he added, "especially likes the idea of so
much room outside."

"We kind of like it ourselves," I said.

Mr. Van Ettig's voice took on a note of warning. "It isn't
every day you find a family that *needs* a house this
big."

"No," I said firmly. "We're *not* in the market. Our minds
are made up."

This latter statement Mr. Van Ettig brushed aside like
a stray curl. "Next spring will be too late. Mr. Wells will
have found something by then."

"I hope so," I said testily. "Because we're not selling now,
then or *ever*."

"You mean," said Mr. Van Ettig frostily, "you don't want
me to bother you any more?"

"It's no bother," I replied. "Call up any time. But the
house is not for sale."

"Well, I guess that's that," Mr. Van Ettig snapped, and
hung up. Half an hour later he called back to apologize for

his brusqueness, to wish us a "Merry Christmas," and to say that if we *did* change our minds about the house, to please let him know at once.

The house is no longer for sale for a number of reasons—nine of them, to be exact. Not that another equally spacious house wouldn't do, but we have waited too long. In eight years the roots have struck too deep.

Once it was "our" house in the sense of Ginny's and mine, and little more than a sleeping place and playground for the children. Now it is *our* house in the full family sense. The children own it as completely as do their parents, and not as real estate but as personal property.

Each day they make another part of it more and more intimately their own. I no longer jump to answer the telephone when it rings, for the chances are the call is for one of the older girls or boys. "Hello—is Danielle there?" . . . "Is Kip home?" . . . "May I speak to Nina, please?"

The children no longer wait outside the bathrooms for their parents to finish. We wait for them.

The bedrooms are no longer referred to as the "one with the fireplace," or "the one over the kitchen," or "the one with the pink rug." They are Kip's room, David's room, Nina and Danny's room, Peggy's room. Even certain chairs in the living room are respected as so-and-so's favorite. Specific closet pegs hold specific clothes. Certain phases of dusting, dishwashing, drying, making beds, and other household tasks are known by the proper names of the children.

"Their" friends are more numerous in the house these days than "our" friends. It is a rare evening when I look up from a newspaper or book and don't see a neighbor's youngster playing with our own, or a rare week-end when new faces

aren't being introduced to me. "Daddy, this is Jennie" . . .
"This is Max" . . . "This is Gordon."

Even the nights are not free from this invasion. Proof of
ripened friendship among the children is "staying overnight."
The more neighbors' offspring there are in our beds, the
happier our own youngsters are.

This, of course, creates certain problems. Notified ahead
of time that Susie from across the road is sleeping in Danielle's
bed, I know what room to steer clear of when clothed only
in shorts or pajamas. But without this advance information
there are apt to be some embarassing situations. One night,
arriving home late from a long out-of-town trip, and feeling
extremely lonesome for the kids, all of whom were sound
asleep, I tiptoed through the darkened rooms and kissed
them all good-night.

As I was undressing, it occurred to me that I had kissed
eleven faces instead of the usual nine.

I nudged the sleeping Ginny. "Say," I whispered, "do
we have company?"

"Billy Oakes is staying with Kip, and the Gilroy girl is
staying with Nina. Why?"

"I'd better learn to count," I said.

In the morning, fifteen-year-old Billy announced that he
had had a crazy dream. Some square with sharp whiskers and
smelling of old pipe tobacco had kissed him good-night. The
boys roared.

The Gilroy girl had had a similar dream.

"Oh," Danielle announced brightly, "that wasn't a dream.
That was my daddy."

Where once our house was praised by friends as being the
kind of big, old-fashioned type we needed, it is now referred

to as the kind that lends itself so well to expansion. The extra porch, which we protect in winter with storm windows, but which we have not as yet heated, will have to be heated now to take care of the rocking horses, doll buggies, electric trains, and wagons that will overflow from Christmas. The attic must be made over eventually. The older boys think they will have more privacy up there. They foresee the time, not far away, when Tony and Tommy will want *their* rooms.

Outside it's the same story. On a bookshelf in David's room are his hand-drawn plans for a chicken house and yard out beyond the garage. We will order the lumber and start building as soon as the snow begins to melt.

Kip is getting in touch with a man who knows a man who can supply us with stock fencing and posts at a reasonable price, and after the fence goes up around part of the meadow, a family of sheep will move in.

At no time more than at Christmas does the house become the property of the children. The general idea is to make it look as little like a house and as much like a window display as possible. Every level area more than a couple of feet square must be covered with some kind of ornamentation.

On top of the old grand piano, which my parents gave me on my thirteenth birthday (in the mistaken notion that I would learn to play it), we erect the "Christmas train." This consists of a flat board base, about four feet square, on which is built to scale a glorified polar landscape of plaster mountains, candy-cane trees, mirror skating ponds, and a miniature Santa's workshop. Around the edges runs the most absurdly ornate railroad ever devised by anyone this side of lunacy. The locomotive is a toy electric engine, done over.

Its cab now boasts a gabled roof, with window flower boxes; the "boiler" glitters with small candies and artificial snow, and a tall diamond stack puffs a great cloud of cotton smoke. Behind it trail flat cars loaded with candy-cane logs, followed by a caboose that looks like a bungalow on wheels, complete with awnings.

Lesser areas in the room support the usual manger scene, and groups of candle-stick angels and choir boys singing before miniature stained-glass windows.

But the broad, generously proportioned mantlepiece becomes the showplace of the room. Each season the display is unique. This year we decided on a street scene from the London of Dickens' "Christmas Carol." For three weeks before Christmas Kip and Dave and I were busy constructing it in the basement workshop. When at last it was finished, it surprised even its builders.

A long row of colorful old house fronts, windows gleaming with red, blue, green and yellow lights, and topped with a profusion of chimney pots and eccentric gables, stretched across the mantle, their backs hugging the wall. In front of them, the mechanism hidden from view by strategically placed cardboard shrubbery, ran two continuous belts at different speeds, powered by an old phonograph motor.

On the slower belt were mounted tiny figures of men, women and children. On the other, travelling at a faster pace, were horse-drawn cabs and coaches. The vehicles disappeared behind trees at one end, while the people entered a brightly lighted church, from which came the strains of Christmas carols, piped to a hidden three-inch speaker from our phonograph across the room.

At one point in its construction Ginny and I were afraid

that perhaps this time we had gone too far. That was when Kip, as a finishing touch, sprayed the wall above the scene with chemical snow.

"Are you sure you can get that off without hurting the paint?" Ginny asked.

Kip looked at her blankly. "Gosh," he said, "I never thought of that."

The ornaments had all been hung, and the presents laid out, and Ginny and I sat alone beside the tree as we had sat one Christmas Eve sixteen years ago, when the presents numbered only two. Now they spread out across the room in a jumble of dolls, doll carriages, tea sets, sleds, train tracks, Tony's home-made locomotive, Tommy's big fire engine, a wagon, ice skates, and half a dozen games.

"To Tony from Kip" . . . "To Tommy from Dave" . . . "To Mary Jo from Nina" . . . "To Kip from Tommy" . . . "To Peggy from Danielle." The To's and From's crossed and criss-crossed each other in a cheery confusion of good will. Ginny and I had long ago discovered that it's much more fun to let the children appear to be the givers than to say simply, "From Mummy and Daddy." It stimulates, we hope, a spirit of giving among the older ones and makes the younger ones feel important, though at times a little confused, as when Tommy will thank Tony for a toy truck which Tony is seeing for the first time himself. "Did *I* give him that?" Tony will ask me. "You sure did," I tell him. "Gol-ly!" Tony will exclaim, marveling at his own generosity.

It was two o'clock in the morning. Tall and fat and overloaded with ornaments, the tree towered above us, its myriad lights throwing bright stains of yellows, reds, greens, and blues on the walls and ceiling.

The younger ones had been asleep since eight-thirty; Kip, Dave, Nina and Danielle had stayed up "to help" as long as they could, but one by one they had dozed off on the couch and had to be led upstairs to bed.

"Next year we'll be sensible," Ginny said wearily, "and set up the tree in the afternoon of Christmas Eve so all the children can help decorate it."

"You're right," I agreed. "It's too much of a job for late at night."

"And the children won't mind. Their presents will be enough of a surprise."

"Of course they will."

Each year we assure ourselves that next Christmas we'll have less last-minute work to do. But as Christmas Eve approaches, we think what a thrill it must be for the kids to come downstairs on Christmas morning and see the room transformed overnight by the giant tree that Santa himself brought and decorated. So we keep the tree hidden until the younger ones are in bed.

Next year, we promise ourselves, we'll be more sensible.

But Christmas, of course, is no time to be sensible. It's a time of unashamed bribery, in which we hope, by a profusion of gifts, to erase from the hearts of our children all memories of unfair accusations, short-tempered chastisements, too-severe punishments, and too-great expectations; in short, to wash the slate clean and build our family relationships afresh. "They'll always remember this Christmas," we assure ourselves, hoping they will remember little else.

But Ginny was worried. "They *won't* be disappointed, will they?"

"Well," I said, "if Tony is still hoping for a life-sized sailboat, and Tommy still thinks he's going to get an automobile with a real engine in it, I guess they'll be disappointed all right."

"That's the trouble," Ginny mused. "It's so easy to let Christmas become a question of how much did I get this time?"

"I wouldn't lose any sleep over it."

"They *will* outgrow it, won't they?"

"If they become parents, they'll *have* to outgrow it."

She was staring at the manger scene on top of the television set. "Darling, can't we make this Christmas the best yet? I mean—let's have lots of Christmas music, and let's sing the carols together and read Christmas stories. Let's be sure the little ones understand the *real* Christmas story." She looked across the sea of presents and shook her head. "Let's try to show them that Christmas is something more than just *getting* things."

She got up and stretched out on the couch for a quick nap before the children's unpredictable awakening. I made myself comfortable in the big chair beside the fireplace.

Suddenly a floor board creaked above our heads, and footsteps descended the stairs.

"Oh, no," I groaned, "not yet!"

But it was only Kip, wobbly with weariness, his eyes almost closed with unfinished sleep.

"It's way too early," I said, and from the depths of my ignorance gave him warning that no presents would be opened until we were *all* assembled.

"That's okay," he mumbled, half awake. "I just want to be here when Tony sees his locomotive."

It was still not dawn when the first stirrings sounded overhead. In a moment the flood of children, shouts and laughter would roar down the stairway and engulf the room. . . .

"Thy wife," says the psalmist in the Marriage Day Mass,
    "is like a fruitful vine.
In the inmost parts of thy house
Thy children are like shoots of the olive,
Round about thy board. Alleluia, alleluia!"

Alleluia!